THE VIRGIN NOW BOARDING

ACKNOWLEDGEMENTS

The fantasy of travelling round the world seems to remain with us all, whatever our age. Although primarily written for the globetrotter, this is actually a book for all would-be travellers – whether 'in the mind' or 'on the road'.

We were fortunate in that, although we were unable to do the trips outlined in the book ourselves (much as we would have liked to have repeated our own teenage experiences – we would simply have been voyeurs!) we were, nevertheless, able to enjoy vicariously the contemporary temptations, via the myriad experiences offered up by those teenagers we interviewed, or those who kept diaries for us.

Some we interviewed before they went – full of fears and expectations. Others we interviewed on their return – full of enthusiasm and tales of deeds done. Their diaries and letters gave us a vivid feel for the experiences as they happened.

The task of thanking all those involved is daunting because like our previous books this is really a book written for teenagers by teenagers. Without the revelations from the diaries, some of them slightly expurgated, of Magnus, Sam, Jonte and Tess, the book would never have existed. We would, among many others also like to thank Cleo, Polly, Philippa, the Emmas, Anna, Alex, Rob, Julian, Simon, Amanda, Mary, William and Saskia for revealing their experiences.

As future consumers of the book – special thanks to Beth, Rachel, Tamara, Gus, Emily and Alice for both their kind and critical comments.

Also Marny Leech, an indispensable part of the team, for her editing and continuing support (this is the fourth book of ours with which she has been involved).

For juicy, enlightening and accurate medical information, we are deeply grateful to Sir David Weatherall and the Oxford Textbook of Medicine, Klim McPherson, Richard Peto, Anthony Storr, Tim Peto, the Cancer Research Campaign, the Family Planning Association, Michael Adler, Helen Kennerley, the Health Education Authority, Oxfam, Paddy Coulter, Di Allaker, Peter Anderson, Richard Mayon-White, British Airways, the Institute for the Study of Drug Dependence, John Collee, Barry Adels, Andrew Freeland and Deborah Waller. Also a special thanks to Tom Paulin for allowing us access to his observations on Indian life.

With infinite skill, the 'I am almost a teenager' Alison Everitt has, with her drawings, exactly captured our verbal scenes as we had seen them in our mind's eye. For all this – thank you.

THE VIRGIN NOW BOARDING

A Globetrotter's Guide to Health, Sex and Survival

ANN MCPHERSON AND
AIDAN MACFARLANE

Illustrated by Alison Everitt

ARROW BOOKS

Published by Arrow Books Limited
20 Vauxhall Bridge Road, London SW1V 2SA

An imprint of the Random Century Group

London Melbourne Sydney Auckland Johannesburg
and agencies throughout the world

First published 1992
© Aidan Macfarlane and Ann McPherson 1992
Illustrations © Alison Everitt 1992

1 3 5 7 9 10 8 6 4 2

Printed and bound in Great Britain by
Cox & Wyman Ltd, Reading, Berks

ISBN 0 09 982910 X

CONTENTS

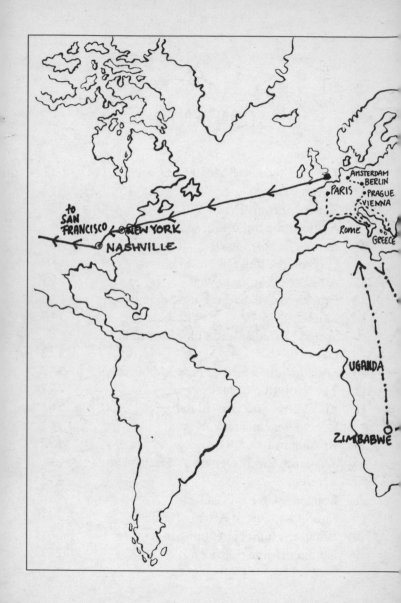

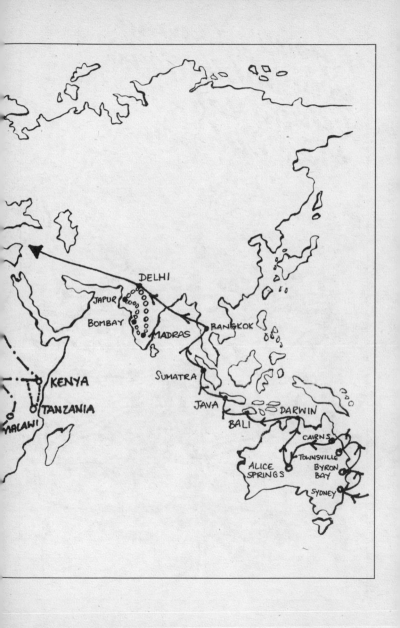

If you're leaving your inhibitions behind, take these with you

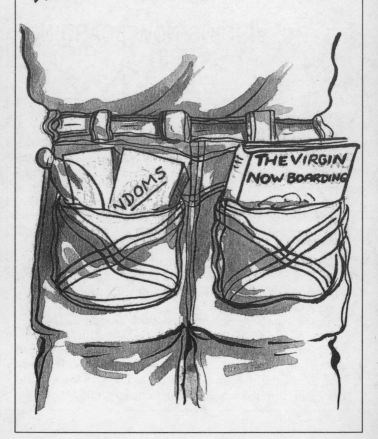

1 THE VIRGINS NOW BOARDING AT GATE 31 . . .

Reality and gravitational forces still held Jim to the ground as he sat writing at Gatwick airport. His plane had been delayed three hours. It had been bad enough fighting his way to consciousness at 7 a.m. to be at the airport two hours early for security checks (a legacy from Iraq and the IRA), and now this. When he'd been delayed travelling with his parents to Majorca, it had been their money he'd spent on the superfluous temptations – Coke, Mars bars, a copy of *GQ* magazine – that he associated with flying. Now it was his money. His parents weren't around, he could get *Playboy* if he wanted to, except that he couldn't afford it. So he had to make do with foul grey water from a so-called coffee machine. ' . . . a cupful of liquid that is almost, but not quite, entirely unlike coffee,' he mused.

Penny's parting present had been *The Hitch Hiker's Guide to the Galaxy*, with the words, 'You'll always be my Arthur Dent, love Penny', written in the front. Although half-way through the book, he didn't yet fully appreciate the deeper aspects of Arthur's character and was still worried about what he might find. Also, his feelings for Penny had become increasingly complex over the last few days, so writing to her wasn't easy.

He ate a Yorkie to take away the taste of the coffee, lit another fag and felt a flash of instant guilt about killing off people around him. If someone had asked Jim, at that moment, what were the two things that mattered most to him in life, he would have first stated to the world: 'Having a totally good time – smoking, getting pissed and making love'; then, after thinking for a long time, and feeling shittily pompous, he would have followed it with, 'and looking after the planet'. Having a totally good time because what else was the point in being alive? As long as it didn't do harm to anyone else – which is where his greening came in. Somehow he had to struggle with knowing that no one in the future was going to be able to enjoy the things that he enjoyed if he didn't think at least a little about what effect enshrining radioactive nuclear waste in tombs, hacking down vast expanses of forest, puffing cancer smoke around and fouling up the atmosphere, and creating whacking great holes in the ozone layer were all having. Minding about what was going to be left for children in the future seemed to him to go beyond worrying about all the disasters – starvation, earthquakes, floods – that were happening in the world now. But no one had asked him, so he kept these thoughts to himself.

He tried again. 'Darling Penny, it's 12 a.m. on the 24th November at Gatwick Airport. I'm not sure how I should begin this letter, especially after what happened the other night. I feel terrific every time I think about it, and then really sad that I'm not going to see you again for months. Mum and Dad have just gone. It was great of them to come and say goodbye, but I'd rather it had been you.' No harm in laying a bit of a guilt trip on her, he thought. 'The plane's been delayed, so they've had to go off to work, but it's actually good to be alone and to be able to write to you. I hope your interview for Africa was

OK. I wish I could have come with you to hold your hand through it all.

'You didn't miss much last night. As usual, Dad saw himself as the ultimate authority on LIFE. There he was, at the end of the table, beard quivering, pontificating about his experiences of travelling.' Irritation at his father's attitudes boiled up again. Why had his father boasted to all and sundry about how he'd given him those packets of condoms? Why couldn't his parents let him live his own life, without interfering? Fifty of them, for God's sake, and called 'Abusers' of all things. His father seemed convinced that Jim would be in and out of every prostitute, on every corner, in every town, in every country he was going to. He was probably getting him to live out his own suppressed sexual fantasies, by proxy.

His sister (an innocent 16) had been appalled by all the talk about sex – and at supper too. If his father had been playing God, then she had been a dead ringer for the part of the Virgin Mary, which was perhaps appropriate as she was a virgin and her name was Mary. She just hadn't been able to understand why there was a need for prostitutes at all. 'Why can't men just control themselves, instead of behaving like bloody dogs. It's degrading women, using them as sex objects, and paying for it. Anyhow, Dad, what the hell are you doing, giving Jim *fifty* condoms? What would Penny say if she found out that you're encouraging this kind of amoral behaviour? Some father-in-law you'd be!' She'd nailed their father to the cross.

Jim broke off his musing and resumed scribbling. 'When we got here, I asked some policeman where "Virgin" was, and he replied, "Sorry, I don't know any." I bet they love saying that. Probably the only joke they know. And anyhow, when we got into the main hall, the so-called "Virgin" lady was about 50 years old. The check-in counter was number 100, opposite TWA and

What to pack your stuff in

Luggage – what has to be 'lugged about with you' - *everywhere.* Get a rucksack or squashy bag that will hold all you need, but keep it small (40-60 litres – depending on where you're going and for how long).

Plus – something like a 'bum bag' to carry your vital stuff in when your other bag has been dumped in a left-luggage locker, hostel, and so on.

What to pack

Most people coming back say they took *too much* stuff and if they went again they would take much less.

• sleeping bag, the smaller and lighter the better (unless you're always going to stay in hostels)
• most valuable is a small thin towel (rather than a large one) – a piece of cotton sheeting will do, and a first-aid kit (see next chapter)
• very few clothes e.g. (depending on sex) one pair shorts, one skirt, one pair jeans, two T-shirts, two pairs underpants, two pairs socks (if you're into them), swimming costume (if you wear one)
• plastic bags, and start with them empty, or with your camera or any other sensitive stuff inside

Don't forget that half of what you need you will be wearing anyhow - like boots or trainers.

Make sure you have something to cover all your flesh if you are travelling in countries where they will be offended by the sight of it, or where the sun may burn it. You can always supplement clothing en route.

Air Europe, and they call first class "upper class" – unbelievable. I had to stand for ages behind an Indian family
with a child hugging a huge Mickey Mouse – it was
bigger than he was. In front of them was this old American guy, with a bike and loaded panniers, a bedroll, a
battered tent, everything in tatters – he was obviously
just going home. I wish I could have picked his brains
about travelling. Right up at the front of our queue,
arguing away and taking absolutely ages, was a woman
like my granny – the same bulging varicose veins – and
a brat in black shiny shoes, jumping up and down on
her bunions.'

Jim paused for a moment to listen to the rumbling of
the crowds around him, and suddenly remembered with
irritation the officious security guard who'd examined his
luggage. He'd asked whether he'd packed his bag himself,
and whether it had been in his care all the time since.
He'd ended up commenting rudely about how shoddy
his luggage was, then Jim had been rude back and the
security guard had put a sticker on his ticket. Well, to
hell with it. Enough writing, he needed a pee. Maybe it
was nerves, or perhaps it was the so-called 'coffee'.

'Good-day. Want to have a fact for the day, mate?'
enquired the Australian next to him, who was also pointing his percy at the porcelain. 'Daya know that the average man takes 46 seconds to pee, while the average
woman takes 79 seconds? And the jokes they play on
you in these places. The dunnies at Amsterdam airport
have little black flies engraved on the china for you to
try and drown the buggers in warm piss; and at Lisbon
airport, the bowls are shaped like lips. Made me feel
excited just peeing there.'

Jim hurried back to his seat, staggering under so much
unsolicited information, but at least it gave him something he could pass on to Penny. What else was there to
say? He was beginning to dry up. What about a bit more
in retrospect? He continued: 'The last two days have

Visas — what for where?

Australia Yes – can get 'Young Persons' work visa –
must show security of £2,000
East Germany No
EEC countries (all) No
India Yes
Indonesia No – up to 60 days. Must have return ticket
Tanzania No – just a visitor's pass
Thailand Yes (unless you're coming from Australia)
Uganda No
United States No – if from England. Enquire if you're
entering from another country
Zambia No
Zimbabwe No

So how far do you actually travel during your flight?

As you orbit around the world in an aeroplane at 1,000
kilometres an hour or so, the earth itself is travelling at
107,000 kilometres an hour around the sun, and at 280
kilometres a second around the centre of the Milky Way.
This means that while you've spent six hours travelling
the odd 6,000 kilometres to America, you have also
travelled 642,000 kilometres around the sun, and
6,048,000 kilometres around the centre of the Milky
Way. Some trip!

been shattering. Getting my visas sorted out was as hairy as hell, even if it wasn't my fault. As you know, it's two weeks since I sent off for my "Young Person's Working Visa" for Australia. At least, I sent off my fifteen quid and cast-iron guarantees that I had £1,500 in my bank account (from all that slavery in the past four months), and what happened? The day before yesterday, they sent back a typewritten note, without my fifteen quid, saying that they needed guarantees of £2,000, and only then could I have my visa. Who do they think I am – Rupert Murdoch? Unbelievable. And too late by then, as well. Anyhow, Jo told me that he'd worked in Australia with just the normal visitor's visa. So early yesterday, I took a Central Line train down to Australia House in the Strand, dropped my passport off, and collected it again, pregnant with my visitor's visa, at about 4 p.m. (Supposed to be the "quick" way of doing it. Took a day!) This all made me too late to get my Indian visa. I'll just have to pick it up somewhere on the way.

'Of course Dad, true to form, pointed out that if I'd done it all two months earlier, I wouldn't have had all this bother. And Mum, just to make sure the point was hammered home with the force of a pile driver, said, "Well you'll know better next time, won't you, dear?". I suggested that perhaps she should have given birth to me when I was already 45, like her, if she's so full of wisdom (I know she's still only 40).

'And as if all the Australian hassle wasn't enough, I've spent days carrying £1,500 around in fifties, expecting to be mugged at any moment before I got a chance to change the readies into traveller's cheques. And then I almost ruined my right hand signing my name seventy-five times. " . . . in the top right-hand corner, dear. And when you cash them, you sign them again in the bottom left-hand corner." Pity Dad couldn't have done it for me, then he'd have had the lecture from "blue eyes" behind the counter, but they don't allow that. She went on and on about how I must keep the copy with the "numbers" on it in some other place – so if the cheques get stolen, I'll still know the numbers. Mum and Dad couldn't believe I'd left everything to the last moment – but it's the way I like to do things, and this is *my* trip.'

Looking up from writing, Jim caught a glimpse of his reflection in the top of the ash-bin in front of him, as he stubbed out his fifth cigarette of the day. Did he really look like that? What a wally. He couldn't believe it. How could he disguise himself? Clutching his rucksack containing a change of clothing in one hand, and his letter to Penny in the other, he staggered into a toilet cubicle. The place smelt like a silage pit, or maybe it was his clothes. Off with the lime-green vest top, off with the black cycling shorts, the white nylon socks, the shades; on with his jeans, his blue T-shirt, and his black socks.

Exiting from the bog, looking slightly closer to a human being now than an android, he found the departure board informing him that his flight was boarding. A wave of anxiety about flying flooded over him, and with the feelings of a condemned man he polished off what might be his final epistle to Penny, declaring, ' . . . I will love you for ever and ever, Jim', before flinging it in an addressed but stampless envelope into a convenient postbox. Nausea gripped him, but to his extreme surprise he still had a passport, it was his, it was current, and he had signed it. He was on his way, or so he thought, stepping through the metal detector.

All hell let loose, flashing red lights, fire alarms – what in ****'s name was happening? 'Excuse me, sir. Could you kindly hold your arms up while I search you?' The guy began slapping his way up Jim's inner thigh – stopping just in time to avoid doing damage. It turned out to be his house keys that had set the thing off. He wondered why he'd brought them with him, except that they gave him a sense of security. If the worst came to the worst, there was one place in the world he could still get into – home. It was the same with his bag. He had been sure his dad's contribution to his welfare wouldn't show up on the X-ray machine – but they wanted to look inside his luggage all the same, and the first and only thing the female security guard pulled out was the packet of 'Abusers', muttering, 'And I thought you were flying Virgin, sir?'

Sweating with anxiety and embarrassed anger after his stupidity with the house keys, he was transported by the shuttle on its little rails, with a weird recorded voice and no driver, to the satellite building, where he discovered his first loss of many to come. His copy of *Hitch Hiker's Guide* still lay, half-unread, on the seat in the airport lounge. He felt as if he'd suddenly and unexpectedly been cut off from something vital. It was like that memorable evening with Penny not long ago, when he'd been allowed his second appreciation of the erection of her left nipple, and somehow had managed to telepathically radio control her right hand down to his own. Much more had started to happen, when they'd suddenly heard the sound of his parents' key turning in the front door. The resulting rearrangements of positions and clothing, and the hasty, embarrassed goodbyes before Penny had departed, had left acres of unresolved, unspoken feelings.

'This is the last call for Virgin Flight 5001 to New York. All remaining passengers should now board via Gate 31.' Had he heard right, was it his flight, where was it he had to go? He'd be the last one aboard, it would leave without him. Leaping to his feet, Jim marched round the circle of the satellite and ran into the back end of a queue of 500 other people with similar misgivings.

At 33,000 feet and six hours later, Jim's eardrums felt like pancakes, with the noises in the cabin coming to him from deep under water. No wing or engine had fallen off, no hydraulic hose had been damaged causing the pilot to lose control, killing 89 of the 230 aboard while

Tips for when flying

Drinking alcohol

Alcohol causes you to pee more, so drinking can cause you to *lose* fluid. Alcohol can also cause hangovers which can make jet lag a great deal worse once you've arrived!

Swollen feet

People do tend to get swollen feet during long flights. This can be avoided by taking walks around the plane; and taking your shoes off in planes is certainly very comfortable. However, for the sake of your fellow passengers, make sure they don't smell.

Hold them under the nose of your next-door neighbour to check – you might get an extra free seat!

Window seats

If you want one, check with the airline whether they take telephone reservations for seats. Most don't, and you have to take your chance. Obviously if you arrive at the airport early, you've a better chance of sitting where you want to.

ALWAYS REMEMBER to reconfirm your flight.
Let them know if you are a VEGGIE.

trying to land – yet . . . yet . . . yet. For him, he thought, flying Virgin was probably highly appropriate, though he remained uncertain as to whether after the other night with Penny he would fully qualify. But hope lay ahead as somewhere out there was a meaningful relationship called SEX. While furtively fighting his neighbour for territorial rights over their shared arm-rest, and during the ritual struggle with the plastic covers to the plastic knives and forks so that he could eat out of the plastic dishes containing the much-desired and long-awaited plastic food, he'd discovered that his complimentary can of diet coke had a number 55 under the tab. Could it be that he'd won a holiday for himself and his future sex object at the Marriot World Center, Orlando, Florida, with ten days of free passes for Disney World?

He searched the can for further clues as the captain's voice started sequencing them into Newark airport, now only fifty-two miles away. A cool American drawl announced, 'We'll have you at the stand at five after the hour.' Small flurries of activity were taking place round the interior of the aeroplane. Children scurried to the 'rest room', quick scribbles were made on incomplete disembarkation cards, overhead lockers were slammed. The girl across the way from Jim had the longest brownest legs, sticking out from the briefest pair of pale blue Levi cut-offs, he'd ever seen. As she clambered out, her thighs almost encircled his head, leaving his hormones fighting for breath and his nervous system fighting a terrible temptation to reach up a hand. He clutched it firmly with his other hand as he collapsed meditatively back into his seat.

2 GETTING THERE

As the plane started to lose height, Jim's mind wandered back to the events that had led him here. Why was he doing this? Christ, what a hassle it had all been, and now, sitting here, a mere fifty miles from touch-down in the States, how far away in the past it all seemed. Six months ago it had never occurred to him that before long he'd be nestled in a Virgin at 23,000 feet and descending into New York. Why should it have?

He'd left school immediately after the madness of 'A' levels, having worked harder for those bloody exams than he'd ever believed himself capable. Not that he'd originally intended to. Many people, his parents and teachers included, had called him 'a waster'; his friends 'dopehead' and 'alchy'; and his enemies 'thick Fogg'. As a result and 'to show 'em all', he'd grabbed himself with both hands and turned on full power – though probably too late. So, while appearing laid back and cool at school during the day, he'd worked non-stop at home, cramming his poor fact-laden brain into the early grey of morning, while pale brown shrivelled fag ends mounted in the soggy bottom of his coffee mug.

During those long bleak hours, his dream had been to

wake up one morning and have absolutely nothing to do but kick a ball around, mend his bike, and slope off to the pub every night with his pals. However, when that single-minded, totally occupying exam madness was over, he'd suddenly been daunted by how much time there was to fill. He had never been so disorganized in his life. Finding a football was too much effort, cleaning his room a complete waste of time, mending his bike impossible. He did nevertheless manage to get smashed out of what was left of his mind eight evenings a week.

Occasionally, in an alcoholic haze, he had begun to have the vaguest glimmers of what he wanted to do (for about a millisecond in every twenty-four hours). Each day, struggling out of bed clutching his hangover, he'd try to get his head together, but the truth was that he didn't have a neurone left working. Every one had been sucked dry of its store of 'nucleotide component' energy. He'd felt battered, bewildered and frustrated. Nothing seemed important enough to try and get it together *for*.

What was worse was that his parents had turned into half-crazed nasties. Barrages of insinuating and insulting remarks about 'finding yourself a job' and 'who do you think is paying all your bills for food and lodging?' had been unfairly flung at him at his most vulnerable moment of the day – between surfacing from sleep at 5 p.m. and making it down to the pub at 6. He'd only been acting like this for three days and already they were behaving as if it was weeks. Why couldn't they have had these arguments with him at 3 o'clock in the morning when he was at his best?

Jim gazed out of the window at a vast carpet of undulating cloud the aeroplane was riding over and remembered how a rolling mass of relief had descended on the Fogg family when a school friend, Frank, had invited him and Michael and some other friends to go camping in the Black Mountains in Wales. He had been driven down by David, in his battered yellow 2CV.

A hangover

Why you get it

No one knows, but it is probably due to the additives or 'congeners' added to various drinks. It is the congeners which help to give drinks their flavour, smell, taste and look, rather than the alcohol itself.

How you feel

You probably know this already but it includes: depression, headache, nausea, dry mouth with a terrible taste, horror of loud noises, and generally feeling fragile. It lasts between forty-five minutes and two and a half days.

How to prevent it and how to treat it

Cold showers, drinking coffee, taking aspirins, Vitamin B, drinking lots of non-alcoholic fluid, all these have been tried but none of them really work. Some people recommend raw eggs and Worcester sauce, others lots of honey. If you have to have a hangover – try your own remedy. Best of all, try not to have *too many* hangovers.

Trying to sober up

However much alcohol you've drunk, your body breaks down approximately one unit of alcohol (i.e. half a pint of beer or one glass of wine) per hour, and there is no good way that we know of to speed this up.

They'd had such a good time – climbing the surrounding hills together, playing football on a tiny piece of green meadow, with the ball continually disappearing down the hillside, and swimming in an otherwise deserted river pool they discovered on one of their expeditions. It was there, lying next to one of Frank's friends, Jane, whom Jim had hardly noticed in school, that he'd begun to feel pleasantly aware of both his own near-nakedness and the near-nakedness of Jane, all vaguely tainted with a sense of guilt about his loyalty to Penny. It hadn't gone any further though – just a sort of unspoken mutual attraction, but the rebuilding of Jim had begun. It was partly envy on his part, as Frank, Michael and Jane, and a friend of Jane's, were intending to take off inter-railing in Europe, and had already bought the tickets.

They were going to start off by heading for Amsterdam, and then move on down to Vienna via a pop concert in Berlin. Then the girls were off to Athens and out to the Greek islands to get sun-soaked, before going on to Languedoc in France to pick grapes, where David was joining them. Jane wanted to improve her French, so she was going to 'au pair' in Paris for a few months, on her own. The boys hadn't firmed up the rest of their trip yet. Jim had realized he was being stupid – at that point he hadn't even thought about going to Greece or France, but hearing about it all, he'd felt excluded and jealous that they'd arranged it all without him. The result had been a jolt to the system that had led him to start translating his own vague ideas of going to the Far East into the most daring expedition since Sir Walter Raleigh's into the cigarette and French fries trade.

The thought of Walter Raleigh reminded him of his feeble attempt at applying for Operation Raleigh. He hadn't even managed to fill in the forms but Jane, as it turned out, had not only applied but had actually failed on the practical course. She was human after all! Lying

Alcohol is not all bad ...

No one should try and pretend that a small amount of drink is harmful. Most people who drink do no harm to themselves. They know their drinking limit and mostly stick to it. There's even some evidence that a little alcohol (up to three units a week) is good for your health! After all, a reasonable amount of the stuff helps you relax and feel good, increases self-confidence, and makes food taste even better!

...But a lot of alcohol is

Alcohol consumption is involved in:

- 50% of murders
- 70% of suicides
- 40,000 deaths in the UK per year
- 1,400 deaths on the road per year
- 20% of child abuse cases
- over eight million days off work per year
- 60% of serious head injuries
- one in three accidents in the home
- one in four emergency hospital admissions
- 17,000 admissions to psychiatric hospitals per year
- 10-25% of patients in medical wards have an alcohol problem
- alcohol also causes memory loss, difficulty in calculating, and indigestion
- of all convictions for drunkenness in males, 21% are of men under 21
- of all convictions for drunkenness in females, 16% are of women under 21

The stages of intoxification

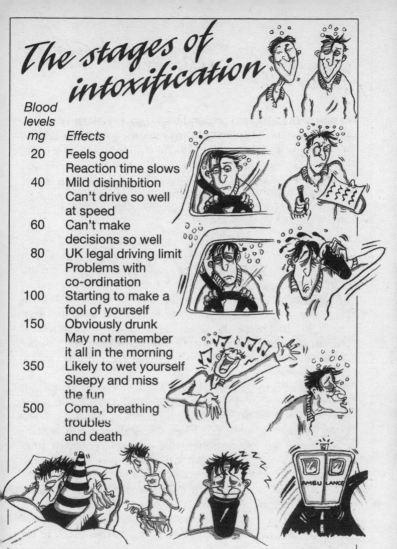

Blood levels mg	Effects
20	Feels good Reaction time slows
40	Mild disinhibition Can't drive so well at speed
60	Can't make decisions so well
80	UK legal driving limit Problems with co-ordination
100	Starting to make a fool of yourself
150	Obviously drunk May not remember it all in the morning
350	Likely to wet yourself Sleepy and miss the fun
500	Coma, breathing troubles and death

Rapid drinking leads to intoxication. Blood alcohol levels in excess of 150 milligrams are associated with periods of impaired or totally absent memory – amnesia, or can't remember a blind thing.

by the pool in the Welsh mountains, she relived the
experience for him as if it had only just happened.

□ □ □

'The night before the selection weekend, I made the mistake of reading the leaflet giving details about the whole
thing. I suddenly realized I was meant to turn up with a
handmade saucepan and cutlery set. Totally panic-
stricken, I persuaded my family to help me and we made
a saucepan out of an old crayon tin, a spoon from tinfoil,
and – the crowning masterpiece – a plate from a hol-
lowed pumpkin.

'Next morning I had a vast carbohydrate-laden breakfast, and then Mum drove me to the meeting point where
forty ghastly, fit-looking boys and girls were waiting,
clutching hand-carved ladles and every conceivable
hiking gadget, and wearing incredible walking boots.
Little me desperately tried to hide the fact that the best
"boots" I had were the ones I was wearing – a tattered
pair of trainers. Then, during the "checking bags" ses-
sion, my poor old pumpkin was classed as "food" and
chucked out.

'We then got allocated alphabetically into teams of
eight and were given thirty seconds to repack the scat-
tered contents of our bags. Each team was handed a tyre,
a ton of planks, what felt like a five-gallon water bottle,
a map, and an incomprehensible grid reference. At first
everyone was in direct competition with one another and
saw the other team members as rivals. Any niceness was
out, or simply a display for the sake of the ever-vigilant
judges who snooped around us non-stop. But it wasn't
long before a mellow sense of unity got established
between us, without any "I'm going to be the one to
lead" nonsense.

'Next in the sadistic stakes was a two-hour plank-
laden ramble over stiles and fields to a seedy cub-scout

camp which was to be one of our bases for the next
twenty-four hours. By then I was so exhausted that I
thought the test was finished. Ah, what wishful thinking
can do! We were immediately made to jog back to our
campsite and were given a huge bag of parsnips, swedes
and cabbages, two dead rabbits, and a match; and told
to light a fire, cook supper, and make a bivi in about one
hour flat. Just to prove how far I'd managed to overcome
my prejudices – even after two-and-a-half years of vege-
tarianism – I set myself the sado-masochistic job of

Unit equivalents of different tipples

1 unit contains 8 grams of pure alcohol.
How many units is your drink?

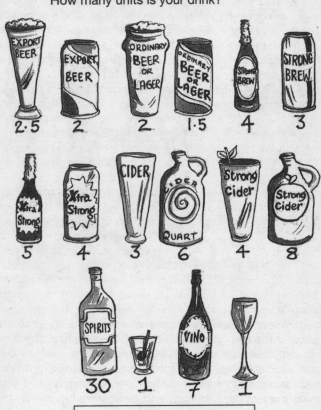

SAFE LIMITS PER WEEK
0-21 units for men
0-14 units for women

skinning one of the rabbits. You wouldn't believe something natural like that could smell so bad. I just about got the skin removed and was enjoying chopping off a leg when I carved the top off one of my fingers instead. Well, nearly. A little bit of skin kept it hanging on – here look, you can see the scar.'

Jim had gazed at the proffered wound, half in pity-laden adoration and half in nausea. 'It poured out blood,' continued Jane, 'so one of the supervisors took me inside. I felt a complete idiot in front of all those macho males and females. Of course, the supervisor then had to decide it needed stitching. It was just typical of me that after a reasonably accident-free life till then, the one weekend I was trying to prove my true grit, I managed to injure myself. The last thing I wanted was a humiliating four-hour wait in the local hospital's casualty department. I even missed supper. The others told me it was delicious, though the rabbit stew tasted a bit off owing to half my finger being in it.

'We spent the rest of the evening (or what was left of it) doing mental exercises, and finished with a discussion group. Everyone had to talk for five to ten minutes on a range of questions like, "Should smoking be banned in public places?" or "Why someone could really hate me" or "My worries about sex". Then at last it was bed. I didn't like being told to go to bed, as if we were children, but boy, were we keen to get there. Everyone was asleep in minutes.

'It felt like about five minutes after we'd all gone off, snuggled down into our sleeping bags, when we were woken again. In fact, it was 6 a.m. and we were made to do ten minutes of star jumps and leap-frogging before each of us had to give another three-minute talk. I suppose these were also meant to have been prepared, but it was another of my last-minute panics. I just rambled on for three minutes about my family, and how mad they all are – not difficult, though I don't think anyone was

Taking a year off

Advantages

- 'gave me self-confidence'
- 'did all sorts of things that I would never have done otherwise ...'
- '... learnt to type and word process so I can always make money in the holidays'
- '... and I tried working at different jobs. It helped me sort out what I wanted to do'
- 'I travelled and saw parts of the world I'd never see otherwise'
- '... made me realize I wanted to get a qualification so I didn't have to do dead-end jobs like waitressing all my life. Though it was fun while I did it, I can't see it being such fun in ten years' time. There were lots of vacancies for skilled jobs,but not much for unskilled'
- '... made me appreciate home!'
- 'when I went for a training job, they were impressed that I'd done all sorts of things. I think that's why I got the job

Disadvantages

- '... was really difficult getting back to my studies again...'
- '... wasted my year off. I had great plans, but I never got it together. By the end of the year, I was no better off and felt pretty pissed off'
- '... was difficult to get work, and the jobs I did get were really boring'
- 'when I got to college, everyone seemed so young because they'd gone straight from school. I felt I didn't fit in and felt like a real granny'
- 'I wanted to get on, and taking a year off would have delayed me'

paying any attention to anything anyone else said. Most people were looking decidedly the worse for wear by this stage: pale and wan and three-quarters asleep. We just stood there meekly, trying to inject a bit of enthusiasm into our contribution, but thinking, "God, how much longer is this going on?"

'After that we made another fire and had breakfast – the best porridge I've ever tasted – followed by a swimming test.

'You won't believe it, but after all this, although we were dirty and wet, total elation ruled the day. Even after what felt like five minutes' sleep, I wasn't tired at all, or so I thought. I just felt great that I'd survived the ordeal. This time it was really over, and we were allowed dry clothes and a vast binge-up. Then my parents came and picked me up, and as soon as I got in the car, the adrenalin wore off. God, was I exhausted, and aching and bruised all over. I have to admit though, I wasn't in the least surprised I failed. I was hopeless.'

That's what she said, but it might have been some comfort to Jim to know that Jane's self-confidence had in fact taken a real battering.

□   □   □

Jim's aeroplane had begun to leapfrog its way over the wisps of cloud, as if it was trying to land on a wintry ethereal landscape made up of cotton wool, with 10,000 feet of air still below. Jim daydreamed on. 'So what about the cash for your world trip? How are you getting that?' the ever-pragmatic Jane had enquired. 'Ah,' he'd sighed, the weight of nineteen years of worldly experience sitting heavily on his shoulders, 'that's another story.'

3 RAISING SERIOUS DOSH

Tiny shudders passed through the frame of the aeroplane as they spun through the clouds, shudders growing gradually into more powerful jerks. The hydraulics smashed the landing gear down, and nervous laughter rippled around. A small child began to cry. Sea, trees, a harbour, then a vast parade ground of houses with blue shells of swimming-pools came up at them through the evening sky – belonging to whom, he vaguely wondered? He began to get that empty-stomach feeling of nervousness – nothing, he told himself, to do with landing. If they were smashed up, so be it. It was the anticipation of coping – away from the crushed slurp of aeroplane life, fighting for one's share of elbow room; away from his cosy family, away from Penny, away from the cats, away, away.

Would his bag be at baggage collection? Did he still have his passport? Had he filled in his 'visa waive' form, his 'I-94 Arrival/Departure Record' form (on which he found a red warning that 'A non-immigrant who accepts unauthorized employment is subject to deportation'), and his customs declaration card (stating that he was not bringing in . . . birds, snails or other live animals – a snail a live animal – since when?) correctly? How was he going to find his way to the Vanderbilt YMCA on 47th Street, between 3rd and 1st Avenues? Would they have kept his reservation? Christ, with worries as numerous as this, why did anyone ever travel?

To take his mind off all this, he drifted back to Jane and her question about money. *He'd* wondered where it was coming from too. He'd intended to work after his exams had finished; in fact, just before leaving for Wales he had fixed himself up with a job at a PGL Adventure Holiday Centre ('Parents Get Lost', as he'd heard it called). It had occurred to him also that he might try and work in America on his way round the world, but he'd also reckoned that this would be a hassle. He didn't want to go through all the bother of getting a proper visa, and anyhow he'd need some serious dosh before setting out. He'd been applying himself to the problem when Frank and Jane left Wales to get organized before the first leg of their trip to Europe. At Newport bus station, standing in a grey drizzle, they'd agreed to keep in contact over the following months by writing to one another regularly about their various expeditions. As it turned out, to date he'd received nothing but a couple of 'Wish you were here' postcards, even though he knew the sods must be back. Frank must be at university and Jane in Paris by now, au pairing.

They had parted, and Jim had been left alone with his money problems. He didn't know much about PGL, but if he was going round the world, he'd better start somewhere. What he didn't want to do was fling himself straight into a permanent job, or even a poly or university, so he'd taken this year off. He had, however, reluctantly, and after much argument with his school and parents, sent off for the UCCA/PCAS form – a form he now guiltily realized was still sitting in the drawer of his table at home. It was supposed to be filled in by mid-December. What if his mother went through his drawers? He wanted the *final* decision to be carefully and rationally thought out. He needed time, two years if necessary, so

First-aid kit for travellers

This needs to be kept in a small waterproof container. A cheap plastic bag or box is fine. It also needs to be kept available, in the stuff you normally carry around with you all the time. If you feel the need to take the whole of the chemist's shop with you, maybe you should think again about travelling!

Minimal kit

Available from a chemist without prescription

- 24 soluble aspirin or paracetamol, packed individually in silver foil (for fevers, headaches, pain)
- 1 Elastoplast dressing strip (for covering cuts, abrasions, blisters, burns)
- 1 packet assorted waterproof Elastoplast (as above)
- 1 packet Steristrips dressings (for holding edges of cuts together)
- 1 packet gauze squares (4 x 4 cms) (for large cuts)
- 1 crepe bandage (for bad cuts, sprains)
- 1 tube Savlon (for helping heal infected cuts, sores, spots)
- 24 Imodium tabs (for diarrhoea)
- 5 packets Rehydrat (for restoring your fluid intake if you've had bad vomiting and diarrhoea)
- 1 Lipsil (for dry lips)
- 1 Factor 14 or above suntan cream or lotion (for good protection against sunburn)
- 3 tubes Flypel (to ward off nasty beasties. Nothing's perfect, but this is better than most)

- 10 x 4 mgs Piriton tablets (an antihistamine for bad allergic reactions to bites and stings)
- small bottle of oil of cloves (to put on aching tooth)
- Calamine cream (for treating sunburn or insect bites)
- HC 45 cream (for itchy bites. Use sparingly)
- Steritabs (to sterilize water)
- Canestan (antifungal cream)
- 1 packet condoms?

On prescription

You may have to pay for these

- 14 x 200 mgs Trimethoprim tablets or other course of antibiotics (in case you get an infection)
- Flagyl (for some types of diarrhoea)

Make sure you go and see your family doctor (GP) at least three months before you plan to set off, to give enough time for all the different jabs you may need.

as not to feel he was jumping on some bandwagon or other because it took his fancy for a moment. If he did that, he'd end up on the other side of the system realizing he hadn't done what he wanted at all. So it seemed a good idea to travel for a while, and with no absolute commitments.

A steady job was tempting though. Take Ann, one of the many in his year who'd done that. She was self-determined and she got the job she wanted in a bank. You could see the point – earning solid money, knowing where she was going, when she'd get promotion. In a few years' time, she'd be a branch manager earning £30,000 a year, able to buy a house, and probably with a company car. The bit of Jim that envied her hadn't really been pushed out till the plane took off from Gatwick. When Ann and some of the others had started jobs, and everyone else had gone back into education at the end of the summer, he'd realized that he was facing something quite different – most specifically a money problem, but also the uncertainty of not knowing what to do with his life.

After three weeks at PGL, he'd got a job at a local wine bar called Grubs. His Tom Cruise barman fantasy had rapidly exploded on finding that his work was actually washing glasses, cleaning up at the end of the day and taking the trash out – not a cocktail shaker in sight. His mum didn't approve. She criticized the way the staff came and went, and 'didn't have any prospects to look forward to' – not like Ann, with her 'good steady job'. But, in fact, Jim's co-workers did all have aspirations. The work at Grubs was secondary to them. Sarah, the hardest worker, was a British champion in the martial arts; Martin, who chain-smoked like Jim, was doing photography; and Bill was saving up to canoe down the Amazon. They all had plans for their lives, but his mum hadn't been impressed.

There had been definite ups and downs. The ups had been the social life, and learning from the other people working at Grubs that there wasn't some secret formula for coping with new experiences which one person knew and everybody else had to guess. It was just a matter of finding out what to do as each one occurred. The main thing was not being afraid to ask if you didn't know. Infinitely better than not asking, and then making a fool of yourself, though he didn't always practise what he preached.

It was amazing. He'd only started working for the money, and had ended up enjoying meeting all the different kinds of people wandering in and out. It was quite a trendy place to be with loud music and mirrors and plants everywhere. All his friends drifted through. When he was working, it absorbed his whole life, like a sponge. He'd always looked forward to the things he could do in the evenings when he left school, but now, working five shifts a week of eight hours – washing glasses, making coffee, sweeping up – completely swallowed his social life. All he could manage when he got home was to collapse, sleep, and then curse when he realized it was next morning and he had to go to work again. The stress had got too much for him and his hands began to sweat and shake, especially on Fridays and Saturdays, when things were at their worst. He'd broken down so badly one evening that Sarah had sat him in a corner and lectured him. 'For Christ's sake, calm down. This is not the be-all and end-all of your life. If you can't take it, just get the hell out.' She'd meant well. He lasted six weeks.

He had been paid by the shift at £3 an hour, with a lot of tips, but finally it wasn't worth it. He felt he was just being used to make money for other people – the manager, the owner of the place – and he hated being pushed around. He knew that neither he, nor for that matter most other people, could afford that attitude but as things turned out, he was late a couple of times, got the push, and started cleaning people's windscreens

Immunizations

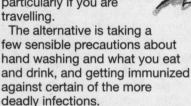

Many serious infections are now preventable. One way to ensure you don't get infections is to isolate yourself entirely from the outside world. However, this is not practicable, particularly if you are travelling.

The alternative is taking a few sensible precautions about hand washing and what you eat and drink, and getting immunized against certain of the more deadly infections.

What is an immunization?

When a bug causes an infection in your body, your body normally produces antibodies to destroy the infecting bug. If the same bug then gets into your body again, the antibodies are already there to kill it off.

The principle of immunization is to make your body believe it is being invaded by the bug, so that it produces the antibodies. However, the immunization injection contains bugs which have been altered so that they don't cause you to be ill. They simply cause your body to produce the antibodies in case you have to face the real bugs during your travels.

What immunizations you need when travelling depends on the countries that you're going to, for how long, and the immunizations you've had in the past. Some immunizations last for ever, some for only a short time. Apart from polio (drops by mouth), all immunizations are given by injection. Ask your doctor for information if you are uncertain about what immunizations you had as a child.

Immunizations for the well-organized and health-conscious traveller

For Africa, South America and Asia

Two months before you go:
- yellow fever
- typhoid (first shot)
- tetanus (booster)
- rabies (first shot)

One month before you go:
- typhoid (second shot)
- polio (booster)
- rabies (second shot)

Few days before leaving:
- cholera
- gamma globulin
- (meningitis - for some places)

Immunizations for the disorganized traveller who leaves everything to the last minute and only half believes the immunizations work.

All at once:
- typhoid
- tetanus
- polio
- gamma globulin
- yellow fever (If you're going to Africa or South America, and *have to have* a yellow fever certificate to get into the country, remember the certificate *isn't valid* until ten days *after* the injection, but it does last ten years).

Regulations

Which countries need which immunizations, and what certificates you need, tends to change. If in doubt, there is an extremely useful booklet, *The Traveller's Guide to Health* (technically called T1) which is free, regularly updated, and can be obtained from your family doctor or any post office.

Diseases

Tetanus – from EARTH and caused by BACTERIA. A nasty illness with muscle spasms and resulting in death. It is rare in Europe because most people are immunized against it at birth, at 5, and at 15, and then again if they are doing something risky, like travelling to the Far East. It is caused by a bacteria found in dirt which gets into cuts and wounds. Have a booster if you are travelling abroad and haven't had a booster in the last ten years.

Cholera – from SHIT and WATER and caused by BACTERIA. This gives dreadful diarrhoea. Some countries insist on a valid certificate before allowing you in. The immunization is not very successful and only lasts six months. The best way to avoid cholera is to be careful with the water you drink.

Hepatitis – there are several types, A, B, C, and others, which affect the liver, cause jaundice, and make you feel tired, weak and ill. Any traveller with abdominal tenderness, tummy ache and dark urine should suspect hepatitis.

 Hepatitis A – from SHIT, WATER and FOOD and caused by a VIRUS. For instance, a cook may have it on his/her hands and spread it to food which you eat. It is especially common in countries with warm climates. It is a good idea to have an injection of gamma globulin containing hepatitis A antibodies, but the injections need to be repeated every six months, so if you're travelling for more than six months, get another injection en route. If you are likely to do this, it's also sensible, because of the AIDS risk, to take a kit of a few sterile needles and syringes, with a letter saying what they're for (or you might get accused of being a drug addict).

Hepatitis B – from having SEX, coming into contact with BLOOD, and caused by a VIRUS. It is usually spread by sexual contact with someone carrying the virus. Condoms will protect you. Beware also of dirty needles, tattooing and ear-piercing. You can be immunized against it, but it takes three doses - the first two a month apart, and the third six months later. This gives good protection, so have it done if you think you are at risk, and unless you're silly, you shouldn't be!

Typhoid – from FOOD, WATER and SHIT, and caused by BACTERIA. The signs of having it include fever, headaches, tummy aches, constipation and diarrhoea. It can be *very* serious. Immunization gives 70-90% protection and lasts three to five years. It is worth it if you're living rough, even if it gives you a sore arm for a day after having it.

Polio – from FOOD, WATER and SHIT, and caused by a VIRUS. It is rarely seen in Europe now because all babies are immunized at birth. It is common in Third World countries where it causes paralysis. The immunization involves a few drops of vaccine to be swallowed, and you only need re-vaccinating every ten years.

Yellow fever – carried by MOSQUITOES and caused by a VIRUS. It is really a disease of monkeys that gets spread to humans by mosquitoes biting first infected monkeys and then humans. It is called 'yellow fever' as it causes liver damage and jaundice. Some countries need a certificate of immunization, and the immunization is only available at certain centres.

Rabies – from infected DOGS, CATS, FOXES and caused by a VIRUS. Rabies is very nasty and is responsible for 15,000 deaths a year world wide. It is worth getting immunized if you are travelling rough in Africa, Asia or India. The virus gets into the nerves and brain (and can take three months to develop).

Measles – caused by a VIRUS. You should have been immunized against measles when you were about a year old. Check to make sure whether you've had the disease. Measles still kills huge numbers of children and adults in developing countries because people there haven't been immunized. Don't travel without being immunized against measles.

Meningitis – check if you need to be immunized against certain bacteria causing this. It depends on the country you're going to.

Rubella, Diptheria, Whooping Cough – check whether you were immunized against all these when you were young

Condoms

Various names for condoms in different countries:

• France: presevatif, condom, capote anglaise, chapeau, imper, galoches, caoutchoucs
• Germany: kondom, pariser
• Italy: condom, preservativo
• Spain: condon, hule
• Holland: condoom
• Greece: prophylactico, capota
• Denmark: kondom, praeservativ
• Japan: kondom
• America: rubber
• Australia: franger (using a condom is 'putting a raincoat on')
• Thai: pung yang a na mai, plok
• India: no word, but use nirodh which is a brand name like durex
• England: condom, durex, johnny, rubber, japanese wrinkly (to name but a few).

instead. Suddenly all the money that came in was his own, and he could work whatever hours he wanted – until the police stopped him. The same day, real panic had set in about his preparations to go away.

Penny had rung and mentioned getting her passport renewed for Africa, as there was a three-month backlog at the passport office. A smug innocent at such things, he'd said casually that luckily his didn't run out until March the following year. As the words fell from his mouth, it dawned on him that he'd be travelling in March! 'I – I – I'll ring you back,' he'd stuttered. Half an hour later, after searching cupboards, suitcases, and jacket pockets, with a pulse rate of 180, he'd finally located the damn thing in his father's chest of drawers in an envelope marked 'Passports'. 'Look Penny,' he had wheedled, a Humphrey Bogart fag hanging from his lower lip, his feet up on his bed, 'seeing as you're going into town to do your own, what about doing mine at the same time? It won't take any longer, and I'm a bit tied up at the moment.' 'Yea,' she'd replied, 'considering how many pints you're going to put away this evening, no doubt.'

Three days later, without Penny but with her passport, he descended from the tube at St James's Park glazedly absorbed in a 'Poems for the Underground' poster, which read:

THE HITCHHIKERS

They burn you
like the berries of mountain ash in August
Standing by the road
clearly defined
autumnal brilliant heads
scorched from waiting
in the sun.
How can

Passports

Full passport

This is what you will need for most travel. It is valid everywhere (though you may need an additional visa for some countries – see Chapter 1). To apply for a passport, you get an application form from the post office. You'll need two passport photos, and the form and one of the photos will have to be signed by a doctor, a lawyer or some other person thought to be responsible who knows you. Your family doctor may charge you for this. Allow *two months* for sending it off and getting it back.

British visitor's passport

This is valid for one year and is available from *main* post offices. But you have to be a British citizen and you're restricted to the countries you can visit. It's no use for visiting the USA and the Far East.

you pass them up?
But you do,
and dream each night of a hell
where you are a hitchhiker
and no one will ever stop
to pick you up.

Diane Walcoski, 1937, from
The Man Who Shook Hands, 18 June 1990

He rounded the corner into Petty France, where he found what he took to be the left-overs of yet another demonstration against the government from nearby Downing Street. It was the tail-end of the queue for the passport office. Three hours, eighteen fags (six of them bummed), and eleven new friends later, he emerged victorious, or semi-victorious, or, in fact, on reflection, almost totally defeated.

It had gone wrong from the start. The harridan behind the desk, finding eight mistakes and three missing statements on his form, had, at first, refused to accept anything – including his passport photograph (taken during one of his more tidy periods) – as relating to him, even if his family doctor had certified the photograph as 'a true likeness'. Penny's forms had been blemish free. 'Typical,' he'd heard the hag mutter. 'Trust a woman to get it all right first time.' Swallowing his rising anti-feminist bile, he'd finally followed the instructions (the only ones it seemed he *had* managed to follow) stuck up behind his persecutor, who definitely wasn't practising what they preached. 'Smiling costs nothing, why don't you try it?' Jim found to his amazement that it actually worked.

□   □   □

'All service trays to be locked up, no smoking until you are well inside the terminal.' Damn, just as he needed a fag, too. 'Safety belts to be kept in the locked position

Medical and travel insurance

The best insurance is a combined one to cover health and baggage. This will minimize your worries if there's a disaster.

Insurance from mainstream companies is expensive, does not cover long periods of time, and is designed for a more affluent traveller than the average student – though the cover is comprehensive and generous. Shop around for the best student bargain and choose a policy to fit in with your needs.

Costs vary, but the sort of figure you'll be looking at (1992 prices) is £40 for three months in Europe; £80 for three months worldwide. Price depends on destination, length of stay, and whether you choose the basic policy or require baggage cover too.

Causes of death when travelling

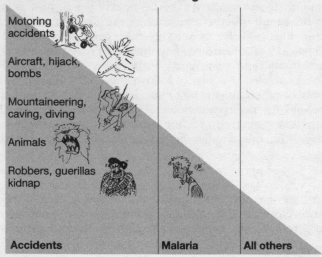

Motoring accidents

Aircraft, hijack, bombs

Mountaineering, caving, diving

Animals

Robbers, guerillas kidnap

Accidents   **Malaria**   **All others**

until the plane has come to a complete standstill.' A schoolmistress-type air hostess told him to put his seat 'into the upright position please'. Sudden irritation took over from anxiety. The 'No Smoking' sign went on and the wing extruded more and more wing until the final thump on to the runway.

He had made it, and he suddenly realized how reassuring it was that he knew at least where his next few nights would be spent. A month ago, he'd rung the Y's Way International in New York, staggering through all of the fourteen digits – 0101 212 760 5856 – given him by Campus Travel, in order to book himself in for three nights at the Vanderbilt YMCA on 47th Street, between 1st and 3rd Avenues. It was going to cost him $42 a night, which seemed hard on his meagre finances, but as the voice at the other end of the phone informed him that the average hotel room in New York cost around $150, and that Central Park was hardly suitable for sleeping out in, given the number of rapes and murders – he took it. It did seem that the Y had advantages, including two swimming pools, a sauna, a health spa and a jogging track. Check-in time was 13.00 hours, and for all Ys in the States it was best to book ahead, but he was told that if he couldn't, then to check in at midday to see if there were any cancellations. Membership of the Y was included in the price of the room, so he didn't have to pay separately.

Perhaps his parents had been right too. They'd got him travel insurance. He didn't want it – he'd never been ill and was convinced it was a waste of money. But no way were his parents going to let him go without it, so he grudgingly accepted the red and blue plastic card giving a 24-hour phone number to ring in case of emergencies. He couldn't see himself ever using it, but for amusement's sake he meandered through the small print on his copy of the form – so small it was almost impossible to read. What he could make out was that he was covered for 'reasonable hospital expenses and treatment expenses, plus,' – and this sounded really ghoulish – 'charges for the transport of your body or your ashes to the United Kingdom, or your burial expenses abroad should you die', to the tune of a total of £1,000,000. It sounded just about enough – maybe he should break a leg to get the benefit of some of it. It would also cover him for the expense of his ticket, up to £1,000 (almost exactly what his ticket had cost), if he had to cancel travelling as a result of illness. His baggage was insured against loss up to £750 (he reckoned that about £45 would actually have covered the lot). He then came to a section headed 'Exclusions'. He was not, it said, insured against the consequences of 'war, invasion, enemy hostilities, rebellion, insurrection. Also wilfully inflicted bodily injury to yourself' – so suicide due to loneliness was out (not that the money would be much use to him in that instance). Nor was he covered for loss, damage or delay due to confiscation or detention by Customs – bloody hell, he'd thought, they think of everything. At this point he gave up reading. All the same, he had to admit that he did feel a whole lot safer having the 24-hour telephone number that he, or someone finding him run over by a bus, could ring in order to claim. He'd heard that in America the ambulance drivers wouldn't even pick your squashed or dying body off the street unless you could prove to them that you had insurance.

□   □   □

The windscreen business, while it lasted, had been profitable. He'd joined forces with Jo, who had been working nights filling shelves at Sainsbury's – until one day he'd accidentally put cat food into the shelves for baked beans. The first week they tried washing windscreens it had rained every day and they'd nearly given up. But on the first fine day they finally went out, feeling totally exposed and utterly unselfconfident – stuttering wrecks making unsure gestures at people's windscreens, begging them to have them cleaned and praying they wouldn't accept. An hour passed. Nobody responded to their offer, people just stared at them as if they were a circus act. Two hours passed. Finally, in despair, Jim picked the youngest woman driver he could find, plunged forward with an agonized expression of embarrassment, and slapped water on her windscreen. Jo, on the other side, wiped his half of it off and with idiot smiles they stepped back. The girl wound her window down slowly, and said very distinctly, for all to hear, 'Shit, at last I can see. Will a pound be OK?' They could have kissed her. The guy in the next car wanted his done, and then a woman, and suddenly they'd been walking tall. An hour went by and they had ten pounds, two and they'd made twenty, three and it was thirty.

Business was great. They'd even had T-shirts and caps made with the slogan 'Vision Technicians' emblazoned across them. Until after two months the police came and told them it was illegal. The next job was sweeping up on a building site, which Jim reckoned must have been the cleanest site in England, though he'd been appalled by the 'on site' racism, the continual references to 'sambos' and 'our black friends'. He hadn't even dared take a copy of the *Daily Mail* to read, in case it was considered too 'up market'. He made do with his boss's *Sun* instead. Then the brickies had walked out because of not being paid for two weeks. They just got their gear and left, so half the site was working double time moving furniture into a building without walls and a roof, and the other half was not working at all. But Jim had his money, and his plans, and was on his way.

☐ ☐ ☐

A younger air hostess stretched and yawned, then stood in the aisle making kissing movements with her mouth while decorating it with lipstick. He watched her start reading a copy of *Flat Finder*, and read bits out to another Virgin. ' . . . had nothing but glass and hardwood floors at £390 a month.' 'Umh, vicious, but hardwood floors, umh, I could do with those, and only twenty minutes down Westway in bad traffic.' Another shapely smear was added. 'Bye, Jennifer, have fun,' pronounced 'faaan'. Jennifer flounced off to shepherd back a wayward passenger desperate for a last pee.

The plane skidded around the runway like a formula-one racing car, while Jim wondered if he'd have enough immediate cash for the bus into New York. Or would he have to live at Newark airport, eating out of trash containers, until he'd collected enough used coke cans? He'd been told you could get five cents each for trading them in – the Mayor of New York's plan for helping clean the place up.

The Grand Prix around Newark airport continued. The girl with the thighs turned out to be Norwegian. The legs were European: it made them even better. 'We Americans are very friendly people. Everyone over here wants to find penfriends.' The guy trying to pick her up, Jim judged, was 40-ish and divorced. 'My wife was Swedish', he went on (so he was right about him being divorced). 'I went with her to Oslo a couple of times – once to a medical conference.' (So he was a doctor – maybe he killed her off.) 'This is my son Josh, he's sixteen. Gets bored travelling with me all the time.' (The guy produced a photograph.) 'Lives in Maryland. If you get a driving licence down there, in the first year there's a curfew when you can't drive after midnight, and you can't buy alcohol until you're 21.'

Overhearing these snippets of casual conversation, Jim suddenly felt jealous of these people's lives. The easy conversation between two strangers made him feel lonely and inadequate. Why wasn't he living such a useful and meaningful life? But then the conversation grew mundane and the sense of inadequacy faded.

4 A BITE AT THE BIG APPLE

The plane finally hit the stand and disgorged its sweating, burdened contents into one corridor after another towards a series of pathetic little queues in front of eight cubicles. Each contained a white-shirted immigration officer, guarded by notices saying, 'REMAIN BEHIND THE RED LINE UNTIL YOU ARE CALLED'. A woman cop, with a gun holstered in rolls of fat, wandered up and down hustling strange groups of anxious-looking outcasts into this cubicle, out of that one, getting them to fill in more forms, herding them back into the queue, yanking them out again, muttering all the while to their uncomprehending faces.

Jim's turn came up. His passport was flicked through, a vast book was flicked through, a computer list was flicked through, a VDU was flicked through. 'What's the purpose of your visit?' Jim paused for a second – was there a purpose? 'Travel?' he suggested. No reaction, just another question. 'How long you staying?' Finally he was dismissed with the first of a thousand 'Have a good day's.

Jet lag

Why it happens?

The body has numerous rhythms - like the release of hormones that bring on periods and the release of the hormone that makes you grow. Others are the rhythms of sleeping and waking and it is these, the so-called circadian rhythms (meaning an activity that occurs about once every twenty-four hours), that are upset with rapid travel east or west.

These circadian rhythms, which are connected with the release of hormones in the body (hence the upset in the rhythm of women's periods when they travel), are also related to the timing of light and dark. Apart from air travel, living in the Arctic or Antarctic, travelling in space, or spending time underwater, can have a similar effect.

EXCESS BAGS

How do you feel?

You feel tired, lightheaded, unable to sleep and not able to think or function well. (That's why heads of state, when they travel, should leave a couple of days before negotiating.) Some of these sensations may be produced or made worse by booze.

What can you do about it?

Well ... there's not much point in trying to stick to BRITISH (Margaret Thatcher, Rottweilers, football hooligans and all that) time – or you'll be having cornflakes when everyone else is finishing a hamburger. Instead try:

• not drinking a lot of booze during the flight (a hangover won't help you)
• as you leave, put your watch to the time of the country that you are going to
• start eating and sleeping according to the new time immediately, even if you have to prop your eyelids up with matchsticks
• when you arrive, go to bed earlier if flying west and get up earlier if flying east

Latest theories about things that help include:

• taking a natural hormone called melatonin - normally produced only at night by the pineal gland in your brain. Some studies show that it helps you get back into your normal rhythms faster.
• the 'lightness and darkness' effects on the rhythms can be helped by doing a Blues Brothers act with dark glasses when you get there.

How long does it take to recover?

It takes different times for different people, but it may take up to one day for each hour's time difference before you fully recover.

He wondered if this was a question too. 'No,' he said, and walked out into America.

He needn't have worried. The bus in from Newark only cost him $7 and took him into Manhattan, the famous shimmering shape of the Empire State Building and the twin towers of the World Trade Center dipping and rising in the distance. The road rose and fell across a deserted wasteland of metal masts and marshes, before sweeping in a complete circle and sinking under the Hudson river through the Lincoln Tunnel, but not before he was treated to a full frontal of the whole blazing West Side of Manhattan. Surfacing again in the thronged mass of the island, the bus swept round in concrete ruts to the third floor of the Port Authority bus terminal on 42nd Street and 8th Avenue. It weaved in and out of lurching herds of other hippopotamus-like buses and past a criss-cross of massive iron girders holding the shuddering building together. One final lurch round the ramps and Jim found himself thrust again into the fragile vulnerability of an outside world full of people with purpose.

A man in a newspaper kiosk sold him a map of the network of squared-off blocks and streets that made up the city – avenues running north-south and streets east-west. He estimated the YMCA to be five streets north and five blocks east. Tired though he was, he walked, sweating from exertion and fatigue, bent under the weight of his backpack, unable to take anything in except a mass of people, vast neon signs, exotic smells, intersections, red lights saying 'DON'T WALK', changing to white ones saying 'WALK', and hands held out with the mutter, 'Spare any change, buddy?'

The seedy neon sign outside the Y winked at him as he pushed his way through the front doors and swung right into the crowded reception area. 'Have ya a reservation?' queried a dark-haired lady in the glaring light. 'Your name?' A pause. 'Sorry hun, we've overbooked.' Vast gloom and doom began to descend on him through the haze of weariness. 'But if ya don't mind sharing, it'll be cheaper – $25 a night.' First lesson of the trip, Jim decided, was not to despair till you have to. 'Fill in the form, please – and do you have some ID?' His passport presented and checked, he finally heard the magic words, 'Your room is 779, take the elevator to the 7th floor.'

The elevator was packed with blue, red and green nylon backpacks, attached to a mass of smelly humanity, some of whom fell out on the 7th floor with him. Room 779 was tiny, with cracked cream walls and chipped red two-tiered bunks. The lower bunk was already occupied by a grizzled figure his own age, who introduced himself as 'Luke' but said no more as Jim hoisted himself into the upper bunk.

He lay back and assessed his position. Tired – yes. Made it – yes. Hungry – yes. Shower – yes. Out in the corridor, clutching soap and towel, his progress was blocked by a young girl, a luggage trolley, and a 60-year-old lady screaming, 'Place is filthy, honey. You're not to use the showers or sit on the toilet seats.' In fact, he thought, as he watched the scummy remains of his 24-hour-old stubble disappear down the drain, the lavatories on his floor, which were mosaic tiled in brown, were clean and smelt fine. His only complaint was slight nervous embarrassment at having to shower with three other bodies, two white, one black. Hadn't he read somewhere that 25 per cent of American males had had some kind of homosexual experience? Though on second thoughts, if he'd been educated in an English public school (instead of at the local comp), that would have been nearer 100 per cent. Maybe the white-haired lady in the corridor was just used to a better standard of living. Even the multicoloured carpets that you could be sick on without it showing, and the odd carpeted wall that looked as if it had been sick on, weren't that bad. All in all, it was just what he wanted – a room to feel secure in, and a bed with clean sheets to sleep in. The figure in the lower bunk was no more than a deep-breathing lump giving an occasional disgruntled twitch, as Jim lay awake feeling the nausea of exhaustion and aware of distant screaming sirens and the slamming of doors in the corridor nearby.

Too tired to sleep, too tired to stay awake, he came to life again at 6 a.m., his mind telling him that this was 11 a.m. English time. The bottom bunk lay deserted, but a TV was murmuring in the corner of the room, asking him to pray to God that he might be delivered from the evil habit of smoking. Five minutes later, Luke slipped quietly back in, dressed in a gold ear-ring, a 501 T-shirt, 501 jeans, and red Converse trainers. He apologized that the TV was on and hoped Jim hadn't been disturbed. Luke was English, had been on the road for eighteen months, and was flying home in a few days' time.

'Shouldn't have started in New York, mate, you're too naive for this place. The way you look, it's like you're holding up a sign saying, "Look, I'm innocent, come and rape and mug me." Me, I left it 'til last.' Jim sensed a paternalism here which could be turned to his advantage. He might be naive, but even he wasn't innocent of using other people. 'You seem to know your way about. Could you show me the ropes d'you think?' 'Yup. See you at 8.30 downstairs in the lobby.'

At 7 a.m., in a continuing mist of jet-lagged drugg-edness, Jim descended to the 3rd floor clutching all his clothes (none of which he had bothered to get his mother to wash before he left), and dumped them into one of five battered top-loading washing machines. From a nearby vending machine, he bought his breakfast of crisps and a coke. The machine had every kind of milk, if he'd wanted milk – low fat milk, 1 per cent fat milk, 2 per cent fat milk, 5 per cent fat milk – in fact, eighteen different milks with everything in the world either added or taken away. He fed the washing machine its breakfast of soap powder, and then sat reading a discarded copy of the *New York Times*. The latest city statistics – that

Drugs

The term 'drug' is complicated by the American use of the term to cover all medicines. Here we are referring to substances which alter people's perception of reality - so, by this definition, alcohol is included but cigarette smoking, tea and coffee are excluded.

Why people say they take drugs

Relaxing
Nice feeling
Makes me feel hard
Makes me feel sexy
Makes me feel happy
Makes food taste better
Gives me self-confidence
Makes me forget my troubles
Helps me get on with other people
Other people are doing it so I should too
Makes me feel as if I'm one of the 'in crowd'

What is a soft drug and what is a hard drug?

The terms are outmoded. Soft drugs used to be those which were considered to be non-addictive and hard drugs were considered to be addictive. However, this distinction no longer exists, as drugs that used to be thought non-addictive actually may be so. In addition, there are now so many different chemical 'drugs' available, that details on the long-term effects of all of them are not easy to obtain.

Why are people concerned about drugs?

• by altering people's perception of reality, drugs make them behave in unpredictable ways which may endanger their own and other people's well-being, and even their lives

• drugs may have other long-lasting unpleasant effects, either physically or mentally

• because society has chosen to make drugs illegal, if someone does take, possess or deal in drugs, they are liable to prosecution

• you may get addicted to them

Obviously, some drugs have worse effects than others, but being on the wrong side of the police is bad for you – whatever the state of your health!

Cocaine is a stimulant made from a white powder extracted from the leaves of the coca bush found mainly in Peru and Bolivia. South American Indians have chewed coca leaves since 2500 BC. It is used by them to help reduce sensations of tiredness and suppress hunger, and it also plays an important part in their social and religious customs.

Cocaine was first extracted from the leaves about 150 years ago, and was used in Europe by doctors as a panacea for all ills, a wonder drug used to treat depression, syphilis, asthma, tummy upsets, TB, sore nipples. The psychiatrist, Freud, thought it useful for curing people who were addicted to other hard drugs. It was only later that cocaine was found to be just as addictive.

The first coca cola-like drink was made in 1863 and

was called Vin Mariani. Coca Cola itself was first manufactured in 1885, and until 1903 contained small amounts of cocaine. In the USA and the UK, people became gradually aware of how dangerous and addictive cocaine could be, resulting in it being banned.

Crack is a type of cocaine. Other names for it are base, rock, or wash. It consists of small bits of freebase cocaine about the size of a pea. These are smoked in pipes, on tinfoil, or in cigarettes.

Freebasing is the process used to produce the cocaine. Cocaine hydrochloride is dissolved in water and heated with a chemical reagent such as baking powder to free the cocaine alkaloid base from the salt. Before this, coca base was made from raw coca leaves and then smoked. Crack is attractive because it is very easy to use. It has been described as the 'fast food' drug. It gives an instant 'high' - no hanging about, but the effects wear off fast too - within fifteen minutes. This is an advantage to dealers. The effects are so short that an addict has to keep on buying.

The effects of cocaine and crack

'To start with, it made me feel great. Gave me something to live for. Sex was great and it gave me lots of energy. Then I began to come down. I had to use it more and more to get the same effect. All my money went on it. I couldn't stop, I couldn't sit still, and I felt everyone was getting at me.'

(John – an 18-year-old cocaine user)

There are lots of nasty side-effects to cocaine which include a dry mouth, an increased pulse rate, sweating, and loss of appetite. Regular users get buzzing in the ears, diarrhoea, a feeling of tightness in the chest, exhaustion, and insomnia. Long-term frequent use increases the side-effects. Instead of a 'high', there is an uncomfortable state of restlessness, irritability, loss of sexual desire, and a feeling of sickness. If sniffed, cocaine damages the lining of the nose. It can also cause persecution mania.

It is claimed that crack is instantly addictive. It does seem to produce a craving for the drug, even after the effects of the drug itself have worn off.

LSD acid (d-lysergic acid diethyllamide) was first discovered by Albert Hoffman in 1938. He was working as a chemist in Switzerland, and had an LSD trip when he swallowed a tiny bit of the drug by mistake. He experienced strange feelings and effects which he thought must be due to the drug, and he continued to experiment on himself and other colleagues. LSD was used to treat patients with alcohol and drug problems in the sixties, and became a cult drug among some student groups, musicians and intellectuals as it gave a wonderful psychedelic experience. US military intelligence thought it could be used for brain-washing or as a truth-drug weapon.

The effects of LSD

LSD works in very small doses - as little as 25 micro grams. The effect is known as a 'trip'. It begins half to one hour after taking the drug, with the greatest effects happening after two to six hours, and fades out altogether after twelve hours. It makes colours look brighter distorts shapes and sizes, and somehow makes things look as though they're moving when they're still. True hallucinations can also occur (seeing things that aren't actually there). People become overly self-aware and experience mystical or ecstatic feelings. They may feel dissociated from their body, become anxious, depressed, paranoid, and feel that people are out to get them.

The dangers associated with LSD use gradually emerged, and although some of them are rare, they are also very serious, including suicide and psychosis (going extremely mad). Sometimes psychosis does not reverse after stopping the drug. These dangers became known as acid casualties.

Amphetamines There are lots of names for these drugs: uppers, speed, pep pills, whiz, blues. They come as tablets, powders, dissolved in water; and are injected, snorted and even smoked.

Ice is a crystalline type of amphetamine and, like crack, has the disadvantage of being highly addictive and cheap.

Amphetamines make you feel lively, funny and over-alert. To start with, it's like having a 'nice' dose of anxiety, but afterwards you feel restless and irritable, have no appetite and can't sleep. These effects last three to four hours, but may go on longer. If you use amphetamines frequently, you may feel paranoid and think people are persecuting you.

Ecstasy is one of the new synthetic drugs that have recently become popular. It is also known as E, ADAM, or XTC. It is a chemical which combines the effects of amphetamines and LSD. The effects start after twenty minutes and can last several hours.

Beware! It is pedalled as a 'safe OK drug'. It isn't. It depersonalizes you and has several most unwelcome side-effects, including high fever and psychotic breaks. Users are beginning to end up in hospital and there have been some deaths.

the chances of getting murdered in the Big Apple were 1
in 1,000,000 per day if you were black and 1 in
10,000,000 per day if you were white – didn't make him
feel any safer. The guys in the shower last night had had
a mean look.

Leaving the Y with Luke, he felt he'd walked into a
Hollywood stage set of New York. Silent cab drivers
swerved and weaved their yellow fortresses this way and
that, masters of the universe of traffic, mounting the side-
walks, slamming to dipping halts, sucking endlessly up
and down on their hydraulics. Steam rising from battered
manhole covers in the middle of the street hinted at some
other subterranean life in progress. Cyclists snaking their
mountain bikes in and out of the traffic were all wearing
masks. Roller skaters and pedestrians were plugged into
walkmans so that it appeared that their brains were battery powered and the headphone wires were supplying
the electricity. Through this throng they dodged and
weaved across to Lexington, down to 42nd Street and
into Grand Central Station. Grand by name, tacky by
nature, he thought, gazing upwards at what appeared to
be open sky but then revealed itself as a dark green
ceiling about a thousand feet up and covered with golden,
painted stars. The scale was immense with a central
podium offering travel information and underground
passages leading off in all directions containing bread
shops, Dunkin' Donuts shops, key-cutting shops, shoe-
mending shops, coffee shops.

A lady at the travel information kiosk directed them
up a ramp back on to 42nd, where they found a Costa
Rican student manning a 'Visitors' Information Center'
barrow covered with leaflets. Jim confessed that he was a
student, a backpacker, wanting to know what he should,
could, might see. 'You're sure, man, that you *are* what
you seem to be?' the PR enquired. 'In this town, no one
is what they appear to be. Sure you're not one of those
crazy guys who wants to bomb students?' Jim felt uneasy

– was the guy serious or a nutter? But the PR was ultimately helpful, covering map after map with diagrams and arrows showing that this was good and that bad. He said the Y Jim was staying at was the best of the five available, and the one at West 34th Street and 8th Avenue was a noisy and smelly flea pit (a fact confirmed by Luke, who'd spent a night there before moving to the Vanderbilt Y).

Heading for the Empire State Building ('better view than the World Trade Center, guys') on 34th Street between 5th and 6th Avenues, they were passed by women joggers with girating breasts and rippling bum flesh. At 9.15 a.m., fifteen minutes before opening, the queue was already snaked back so they stood in line waiting, while Luke offered Jim the kind of world-weary advice concerning street credness that a nineteenth-century explorer might have offered to an apprentice leaving on his first expedition.

Luke had worked illegally as a bricklayer, crewing on boats, washing up – usually at about $8 an hour, all over the States, using made-up names and social security numbers. They nearly caught him in Florida as the social security number he'd used belonged to a local.

Jim and Luke reached the ticket office, surrendered $3.50 and discovered a further queue for the first elevator to the 80th floor. Luke continued, 'I used to stay in Salvation Army hostels when I had no money. Real doss houses, but the food and beds were free. The Ys are fine, though I tended to hitch everywhere and was often offered a bed by whoever gave me a lift. I wouldn't say it was always safe. One time I got picked up by a gay guy who wouldn't lay off me. I finally had to mace him. I was given the stuff by a girlfriend. It's illegal, but I maced this guy in the eyes and got out of the car fast, threw the can away and ran. The other thing to look out for is drugs. The scene is heavy everywhere. I could take you round the corner and get you anything you want. In mid-America it's mainly marijuana still, because they're ten years behind. On the West Coast it's speed. You can buy a crystal — enough for three people to sniff — for $20. Some travellers are doing it just for dope — one long trip. But if I were you, I'd stay right away. In my experience, it's always a hassle.'

They swapped elevators and were on their way to the 86th floor and out on to the observatory platform. 'Christ Almighty,' exclaimed Jim, 'it's fantastic.' He gazed in amazement down on to the girating air conditioners of the dark-roofed buildings below, across the Hudson river to the west, over the East river to the east, and up to Central Park in the north, the odd helicopter chopping up the air below them. Luke, silenced for a moment, chewed meditatively on his gum before starting up again. 'As I was saying, America is not a cheap place, and you can't sleep out on the streets or in parks, like you can in Europe if you have to. If I were you, I'd beat it as fast as I could for the Far East, where you can eat and sleep for weeks on end for practically nothing, and everything's so way out it's like being on another planet.' To Jim, America was already like another planet.

Back at street level and out on to 5th Avenue, they crossed over and into the familiar and comforting arms of a McDonald's. That afternoon Luke took him to the Metropolitan Museum of Art to see some pictures by a guy Luke referred to as 'a real cool dude' — a painter called Monet whom he'd discovered in the Chicago art museum when he'd ducked into it out of a rainstorm. Having gaped a bit at so much culture, and the number of people who were into it, Jim left Luke with his hero and, on Luke's advice, walked into Central Park at 72nd Street, where he found the Loeb Boathouse. He was famished again, but the restaurant there wouldn't look at him (not that he had the money) because he didn't have a jacket, which a notice said was required. Round the back, however, a fast food service supplied him with chicken strips tasting of burnt plastic, more coke and delicious French fries.

Luke had said the boathouse hired out bikes at $6 an hour and they did, winter and summer unless it rained or snowed. They were ramshackle old things by any standards but the brakes and gears worked, and so did his legs. Again the obligatory, 'Got some ID?', so he surrendered his local video club card and set off, over-taken by roller-skaters and by what appeared to be cross-country skiers on roller skates but with all the wheels in a single row. *He* just about managed to keep up with the jogging flabby bums. As he was meandering meditatively down the West Side of the Park, past the Natural History Museum hidden behind the trees, his concentration was momentarily distracted by a cruising patrol car, the only car he'd seen in the park, and he hit the kerb.

But he was still conscious and there was only a swimming pool amount of blood. Lying there and viewing the world from a great distance, he watched the police get out of their car and bend over him muttering things like, 'Better get this freak into an ambulance,' and 'Maybe he needs a CAT scan.' Dollar signs began to roll up in front of Jim's eyes, even though he knew he was insured and was thankful for that. 'No,' he shouted, 'I don't need a hospital, I don't need a doctor, I don't need a CAT scan. I'm fine, thanks.' They gazed doubtfully at him, as did a couple of passing medics, also seeing dollar signs – but in their own bank accounts. Jim staggered to his feet, established the bicycle was still working, and in a state of dazed self-consciousness pedalled away into the blessed anonymity of the park.

Next morning he again woke early. Very early. His dad would have been pleased. How were Mum, Dad and Penny? Perhaps he'd send them cards just to show them he'd done it. They never thought he would. He'd had his own doubts too, sometimes, but here he was, in New York, which was more than the rest of his family had

Are you what you eat?

There is strong scientific evidence linking food with certain diseases. For example, lack of iron in the diet causes anaemia and slow development in children, and the amount of salt you eat may raise your blood pressure. However, the extent to which diet has an effect on your health is complicated by a lot of other things, like what genes you inherit, what sex you are, whether you smoke, how much exercise you take, how old you are, and so on.

So what is a good diet? Most magazines and health freaks go on and on about what you should or shouldn't eat. No one really knows the answer, but it is as much a question of *how much* you eat of various things as *what* you eat. It's a matter of balance. Throughout the world people eat very different foods, and most of them are OK. Basically you need enough food to give you the energy to do things, and you need enough other nutrients – probably about fifty of them – to keep you healthy.

There's no one food that does it all. There are general guidelines about what's good and what's bad, but that's probably as far as it goes.

The basics of a good diet
• fruit, vegetables and salad: eat as much as you like.
• bread, cereals and potatoes: satisfy your appetite for these, which should provide 50-70% of daily calories. In the UK on average only 25% comes from these at the moment.
• meat, fish and dairy foods: choose carefully to avoid fat, which should make up no more than 30% of your daily calories. That's around 75 gms for men and 53 gms for women – whereas in the UK men actually eat 100 gms and women eat 70 gms.
• oils, butter, margarine and spreads: eat less of these, and you'll eat less fat.
• salt and sugar: you get all the salt you need per day just by eating bread and cereals, so you're probably eating far too much salt. All the sugar you need is in the natural substances you are eating already. You shouldn't need to eat refined sugar.

ever done. The day spread out before him but he was tempted to curl up and stay in bed. His head still hurt and there was blood on the pillow. Stupid fool that he'd been. He should have been part of a gang rape or a dramatic mugging, not falling off a bloody bike.

The bunk bed jolted and swayed as Luke rolled out on to the floor. 'Wanna come and do some of the real New York? No more of this touristy stuff. That's for the birds. I'm off to the Village today, where it's all happening.'

Twenty minutes' walk took them across to Times Square, which with all its seediness, signs and street-sellers had nothing to say for itself. They plunged down into a network of filthy, urine-smelling passages and caverns echoing with the screeching sound of subway trains creeping around curved metal tracks. It was like being in a huge barred prison, a hell that steamed out into the streets above. Jim discovered that his transportation tokens covered both buses and the subway – but at $1.15 per token, getting around New York wasn't going to be cheap. Up stairs, through gates, down stairs and around corners, they discovered the NR line and were eaten up by one of the screaming monsters.

An advert on the subway train read: ''Roaches showed up at our dinner party again for my husband's boss. It won't happen again thanks to COMBAT.' Jim imagined an 'action man' figure, flame thrower draped casually over the shoulder of his immaculate dinner jacket, bursting into the dinner party yelling, 'Stand back, I'll get them measly bastards for spoiling your dinner party, m'am.' Sizzle, sizzle. Another said: 'Drugs again – fired again. How can I ask my family to understand? Phone 212 262 2000.' But the one that made him squirm the most was, 'Anal warts, fissures, haemorrhoids, treated in minutes with lasers. Call Freefone 1.80. M. D. TUSCH.' 'Action doc' at it again, sizzle, sizzle – but this time with a laser. It somehow seemed dead appropriate that this

ad was next to one about how to use condoms so as not
to get AIDS.

They were finally regurgitated at Princes Street. Freed
from anal warts, 'roaches and AIDS they emerged blink-
ing into the sunlight. The streets were smaller here, the
buildings lower, cosier and of red brick, with a network
of intricately designed fire escapes lace-working up their
sides. A nearby doorway contained a cardboard-box
haven enveloping a half-sleeping figure. There was a
message propped outside reading, 'How can you worship
a homeless man on Sunday and ignore one on Monday?'
A poster above read, 'We live in a free country where
nothing is cheap.'

The place had an 'old world' feeling about it. Little
corner shops were spread with fruit and flowers; whole
walls of buildings were painted to look as if they had
windows – flowerboxes and all. Looking south along
each Italianate street strung with lights, the towers of the
World Trade Center gleamed: stark space ships against
the blue sky. On Beedecker Street they sat outside
Figaro's Café, burning their mouths on too-hot cappucci-
nos, gazing at the other drinkers, all of whom (according
to their guidebook) were meant to be writers. Like hell
– they all looked out of work, but maybe that's what
writers look like.

Wandering around, it began to feel familiar. Old, rich
New York women with mouths like puckered bum holes
were yattering away, gesticulating like backgammon
players in a Greek café, false teeth clicking. They had
uniformly wrinkled brown skin and darkly mascarared
eyes hidden behind shades, and they were all having
intense conversations – about what Jim and Luke mused?
Their cats, their grandchildren, their clothes? Covered in
glitzy pink, they tottered along with wide-based foot-
steps, clutching at each other for support. Did these senile
children actually sport incontinence pads beneath their
glamour, and would these too be sequinned like their

Sperm (gunk, cum, semen, spunk)

An average human male ejaculates 2 to 5 ml of semen, which can contain a total number of up to 500 million sperm. (It varies from 40 to 100 million sperm per ml.) If each sperm met an egg, there would be a horrific population explosion – enough to populate the whole of the USA at one go. As it is, 1,000 - 2,000 spermatozoa actually get as far as the Fallopian tubes and only 1 (occasionally 2) fertilize the egg.

Dog shit

British dogs make about 250,000 tonnes of it a year. Dog shit is not only smelly and disgusting, but you can get infected with toxocara – a worm which lives in the dog's guts. The trouble starts if an egg gets into your eyes via your bloodstream when it can (occasionally) cause blindness.

clothes? God, could it be that he'd be old like that one day?

From these old ladies, they made their way south, catching a Number 1 subway train to Battery Park. They bought more tickets, queued again, caught a boat, and after further endless queueing, climbed up the Statue of Liberty's skirts. No incontinence pads here, but the smell was much the same, climbing up 360 steps breathing in other people's stale halitotic breath, in order to stare down from inside her tiara on grey harbour waters.

The trip out to Staten Island for 50 cents turned out to be better value. Waiting in the innards of the ferry hall, skateboarders, cyclists, guitarists, Ivy League undergraduates – the hotchpotch of people who represented New York – again descended on them. A surge carried them all on to the ferry, across its apparently seamless link with dry land. The gap opened up and the whole ship thrummed with energy as it plied its way through foaming waves, past Ellis Island, past the Old Lady, past numerous barges pushing and pulling with determined purpose, seagulls soaring and swooping downwards behind them. The spray tore into Jim's skin as he and Luke stood at the stern clutching their cans of Bud.

Up town, outside the Y, he noticed the signs clearly stating: 'Fine $100 for allowing your dog to foul the sidewalk'. A tiny, tottering, creased old lady, with diamante glasses and a $1,000 dress, slowly drew a transparent plastic disposable glove on to her right hand and popped her huge Alsatian's extensive steaming shit into a 'pooper scooper'.

Having collapsed exhausted back on his bunk, Jim slumbered briefly, before they both set off again for a vast, seedy cinema across the way from the bus terminal on 42nd Street and 7th Avenue. Almost the entire clientele, at 2 o'clock in the afternoon, were down and out, and smelling of pee, dope and poverty – including a man dressed in all-black cycling gear, with his bicycle on the seat next to him. A couple were asleep two rows in front of them, leaning on one another's shoulders, continually shifting to try and get comfortable. Sitting next to them was a family of four, complete with one-year-old child, watching the most appalling violence in a rave-reviewed sensational film. Some people obviously lived there all day and the huge curved expanse of screen, when lit up by white, showed evidence of the endless food and drink that had been thrown at it. Each seat was a miracle of patchwork vinyl, laced together by some crinkled Harlem granny sitting night after night darning away, innocent of the on-screen bloodbath. The place was air-conditioned ice cold, and Jim would have been convinced that they fed pee into the air conditioning if the floor hadn't been slippery with the stuff mixed with discarded popcorn.

Jim was up again at 7 a.m. next morning, but was alone as Luke had flown home the previous evening – back to family, back to England, disappearing on the Newark bus. He left Jim an agenda for the day, beginning with breakfast/lunch/tea/supper combined – juice, coffee and two eggs easy-over for 99 cents at a local cafeteria. Before he got there, however, a demographic time bomb lay waiting for him at the front desk. On enquiring about mail, he'd been handed a square of cardboard, totally black on one side and with two words written in Penny's handwriting on the other. The words said, 'I'm late.'

His mind reeled, his brain cells sweated. Couldn't she have just forgotten to write the rest, like 'I'm late in writing', or 'I'm late hearing about my Africa trip.' No way could it mean what he knew it meant: 'My period is late, I may be pregnant, you're a shit, and you're definitely responsible. One of your nasty little sperms has crawled up inside me, and now look what's happened.' But, he argued with himself as he slumped miserably on to the cafeteria bench, suffering an instant spasm of anorexia nervosa, she couldn't have got pregnant by him. He hadn't actually, well, come, sort of, inside – though at this point he wasn't quite sure what had happened and where he had come. Could they have crept in from outside? He knew they had tails and could swim – but surely that would be the equivalent of swimming twenty miles on dry land followed by forty miles through fluid, wouldn't it? After all, he thought ruefully, identifying with Woody Allen, the only time he'd actually been inside a woman was yesterday, when he climbed the Statue of Liberty.

He wandered dejectedly down to Bloomingdales on Lexington and 59th, where there was someone of his own age sleeping on the pavement at 10 a.m., lying beneath a window piled high with diamond bracelets and necklaces in burst after burst of dazzling extravagance. The guy was curled up, covered by a filthy eiderdown, with his head on an even more filthy pillow, his cocoa cup by his side for passers-by to throw money into. He wasn't unshaven, he didn't look ill – just dirty, with his life history written on a large sheet of paper propped against his body.

> I WAS AN UNWANTED CHILD, THROWN OUT BY MY MOTHER WHEN I WAS 12. I'VE NEVER MET MY FATHER. I'VE BEEN IN HOSPITAL BECAUSE I WAS ON DRUGS. IT WAS MY ONLY WAY OUT OF THIS CRAZY WORLD. I HAVE NOWHERE TO GO. I CAN ONLY LIE HERE ON THE PAVEMENT AND HAVE YOU PUT MONEY INTO MY MUG AND HOPE SOMEONE TAKES PITY ON ME.

Was this the future for his child if Penny was pregnant? Dark feelings of despair washed over him. The whole city stank of seediness and aspiration. At one end was poverty, dirt, the sleazy beggardliness of it all, and at the other the most appalling 'I'm the best, and don't fuck me over with moderation' feeling. In short, everything and nothing was a problem here. You just needed to have lots and lots of filthy lolly and not have the possibility of your girlfriend being pregnant.

He needed to get out. Even if the Big Apple wasn't rotten, he needed to Greyhound it out. He needed to keep moving. He needed to distract his mind. And then there was the question of the letter which had arrived with Penny's card. He hadn't even looked at it yet.

5 EUROPE EXPOSES ITSELF

It was from Frank. Across the back was scrawled, Sender: Frank Boston, 16 Featherfield Gardens, London SE16. The last time he'd seen Frank had been at Newport bus station, four months ago. He'd been jealous when he'd waved Frank and Jane off to London, his imagination playing havoc with him over what they might get up to in Europe, and now here was Frank writing to him in America, raising all his feelings of anxiety again. How the hell did he know where he was, anyhow? He tore the letter open as the Greyhound whisked him along shiny wet roads through dismal New York suburbs. Could he cope with any more shocks to his shattering concepts of love and romanticism? He took a deep breath and read the long letter on and off during the journey, pausing only when travel sickness threatened to overcome him.

Travelling by rail in Europe

Inter-Rail gives anyone under 26 the opportunity of up to one month's unlimited travel in twenty-four countries in Europe, with stop-overs anywhere en route. In 1992, the cost of an Inter-Rail card was £180. You need to take a valid passport with you when you buy one. If you lose your Inter-Rail card, you can't replace it. Various ferry companies give discounts to Inter-Rail card holders.

What are the facts about pornography?

What is it?

A dictionary definition is: 'The explicit representation of sexual activity visually or descriptively to stimulate erotic, rather than aesthetic, feelings.' Erotic means 'causing sexual excitement or desire', and aesthetic means 'concerned with or sensitive to what is beautiful'. By the above definition, many PG films nowadays could be classed as pornography.

In fact, terms like 'pornography', 'erotic', 'aesthetic' all mean something different to different people.

Does it do any harm?

At one extreme, the creation of pornographic material may use and abuse women, children and men, involve extreme forms of violence and be totally exploitative. At the other extreme, as suggested above, even PG films show the odd kiss or bit of flesh. Is that erotic? Is that pornographic? Different people have different opinions. Who should decide?

Is there any evidence about what effects it has?

The anti-pornographers argue that it leads people to commit sexual violence, like rape, and that it debases sex. The pro-pornographers say that there is no evidence for this and argue that it acts as a safety valve and diminishes the number of sexual offences. The evidence from research is very confusing.

Extremely explicit, violent sexual acts are probably bad, whereas the odd bit of flesh in a PG film is probably not – what more can one say?

Who should decide what is pornographic?

Perhaps the real question is, 'Has anyone the right to tell us individuals what we can and cannot watch, read or listen to? (Should there be censorship in fact?) The answer is probably 'yes', if making the pornographic material being watched, read or listened to involved the exploitation of women, children or men; or if watching, reading or listening to the pornographic material leads to violent and/or exploitative acts.

26th November

Dear Jim – Sorry I missed you. I meant to contact you when I got back, but as well as having to get things together for university I had to go and stay with my father. How's life with you? Your sister gave me your address.

It's been tough being back. Suddenly you're not moving so fast. My mind was totally alive when travelling – you'll know what I mean. When you come home, you're in one place and things aren't happening in quite the same way. Life seems slow – even though Leeds is a great place to be at university. The other thing is, no one up here wants to hear about my trip any more. But I have to tell someone, so 'it's got to be you'. You'll have to take all this on board!

After we left Wales we spent a bit of time getting our act together before setting off from Liverpool Street at the beginning of August. 'We' being the four of us – me, Michael, Jane, and a friend of Jane's called Kate who I hadn't met before and who turned out to be a source of potential conflict. We'd roughly decided on our route but didn't intend necessarily to keep to it. We were planning to see how things worked out as we travelled.

First we headed for Amsterdam – by train from London and then by ferry from Harwich to the Hook of Holland. We didn't book, but managed to get seats on the train even though it was solid with backpackers. They were all about our age, mainly English, and heading for the same concert in Berlin that we were making for.

On the first evening in Amsterdam we discovered the 'Sleep Inn'. It's like a youth hostel but has vast great dormitories with 100 beds or more – mixed and no privacy, all of us standing around in our underwear – a great sight, but then that's what travelling is all about. I really liked the atmosphere – very Amsterdamish, and only ten minutes' ride on a tram from the station. We'd started by looking at the youth hostels but they were all fully booked. It was the people at the Ys who suggested this place. It always has beds, being so big. Next time I'll go there by choice, just for the ambiance: pillars, high roofs, lots of glass, but run down and safe. Our luggage was secure too. Amazing how much that mattered – the luggage. If it was safe, then we felt safe, and happy. This Sleep Inn place had showers and toilets, but the mattresses weren't that good. Michael and I slept there one night only, and the girls two. The second night we slept in a park to save money, but in the morning we came back and had a shower and used all the facilities. It was the first time sleeping out for us both and we were dead nervous. Welsh hills and sheep shit are one thing, this was another.

Next day we tried to see the Van Gogh Museum but it was booked up for two or three weeks ahead because of some special exhibition. That was annoying, so we took in a live sex show to compensate. A different kind of exhibition – and no problem finding one or getting in. They're everywhere. Ours was called the Moulin Rouge (the Dutch blaming sex on the French as usual). We all went to it, though the girls were a bit reluctant. We persuaded them by saying, 'If you're going to travel, you've got to take in new experiences. Otherwise what's the point?'

It was in the red light district with all these prostitutes sitting in the windows selling their wares. The whole show lasted an hour and a half and had three acts. I won't go into too much detail (bloody hell, I hear you say, just when we were reaching the good part). First was just a stripper who then invited two males on to the stage, stuck a pen somewhere, and used it to write 'I love you' on the two guys' chests. The second act was a big black woman with a banana. Don't get overexcited. As I said, I'm not going into details. The last act I didn't really like at all – it was a pretty distasteful live sex show. You could tell it was an act. They weren't enjoying it.

Pros and cons of legalizing drugs

The arguments given for legalizing drugs

• there are legalized drugs already, like alcohol
• smoking cannabis is no worse than smoking tobacco
• if it's legal then it's no longer 'wicked' and therefore less exciting
• taking 'soft drugs' like cannabis doesn't lead on to taking 'hard drugs' like heroin
• by legalizing drugs, you do away with the criminal elements that are there at present because of the profits to be made

The arguments given for not legalizing drugs

• more people will take them
• more people will get addicted, and there are more than enough people addicted to drugs, including alcohol and nicotine, already
• if you start taking 'soft drugs', you may move on to 'hard drugs'
• even cannabis has some bad side-effects, like loss of memory
• alcohol and tobacco should be made illegal as well

Facts about caffeine

Coffee, tea, Coca Cola, and cocoa contain a group of drugs called alkaloids, the most important of which is caffeine. This stimulates your brain and prevents tiredness. Caffeine is a mild drug. If you drink a lot of it, you may get anxious, jittery, panicky and shaky, suffer sleeplessness and a rapidly beating heart.

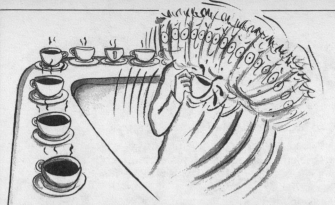

The average amount of caffeine in a strong cup of tea is 50 mgs, and in a strong cup of coffee 100 mgs, though this varies according to the type of tea or coffee and how long it is left to brew. A can of soft drink contains 35-50 mgs of caffeine.

You may be affected by 50 mgs of caffeine but only become aware of the effects when you've had 250 mgs.

Effects of doing without sleep

Everyone requires a different amount of sleep. Seven and a half hours is about average, but some people need more and others much less. Being deprived of sleep doesn't seem to do permanent damage, though it does make you feel terrible at the time. It's difficult to generalize about sleep deprivation. Some of the evidence on the effects of it is associated with all sorts of other horrible tortures that prisoners are put through. A few days without sleep certainly makes you feel tired and irritable, and gives problems with concentrating and remembering. These symptoms disappear after some sleep.

They were just doing it to get money. The man was so floppy he couldn't manage to put it anywhere. He'd probably had to do it four times already that night. Not a job I'd want to have. I worried a bit about what the girls felt about it. They looked grim on the way out but didn't care to discuss it.

By the way, pot is virtually legalized here, though they come down very heavy on anyone using other drugs. I mean, the Sleep Inn had a booth on the way to the dormitories with a menu of the different types of grass they were flogging. It was right next to the tourist information service where we discovered you *could* buy tickets for the Van Gogh exhibition. (That was on the last day. If you don't ask, you don't find out!) You could also buy a three-day public transportation pass and get a vast amount of other information about where to visit. I was on a very tight budget of £10 a day, which is why although the place only cost about £4 a night, Michael and I slept in the park the second night. I had got £90 from my parents, and had earned the rest. The Sleep Inn was a good place to eat – definitely a good deal all round. I did use some money for grass though. Not much. We smoked it that night in the park. I know you totally disapprove, though I can't see why you smoking normal fags is any better. Amsterdam is a very relaxed place. You can get high just walking down the street.

After Amsterdam we hitched to Berlin rather than taking the train. We split up into two groups and tossed for the first lift. Michael and Jane won and got a lift with a rally sports driver. When Kate and I started hitching, we had to wait two hours and then they only took us 100 miles. Even so, we felt we had a duty to entertain the guys who drove us. The trouble is I don't speak Dutch – and felt a shit that the English always expect everyone to speak our language. After that we took the train. We got to Berlin at 6 a.m., before the luggage place had filled up completely. We met the others in the shopping centre where we bought the tickets for the concert. (You remember in Wales we were talking about the fabulous Simple Minds concert that we were going to try and get to see in Berlin. Well, we made it!)

Met up with various guys who'd been on the Harwich ferry. We had loads of coincidences like that. We met Tom in the train station in Venice, Michael met Charlie somewhere in France, and at the concert in Berlin, while all the lights were flashing and things were warming up, Michael asked the guy next to him where he lived. He said Peckham! 'What do you do?' 'I'm a student.' 'Where?' 'South London Poly.' 'What are you studying?' 'Teaching course.' It turned out that one of his lecturers was Michael's mum, and she'd just failed him!

We never got to see the remains of The Wall because in the centre of Berlin it's all been torn down and flogged to the Americans in two-ton pieces at a couple of thousand dollars a time. Kate and me had a bit of stress in Berlin. I think Jane's parents gave her the impression that

More on drugs

Heroin

Heroin is one of a group of drugs derived from the opium poppy. Opium is the dried milk of the opium poppy, and contains morphine and codeine. Heroin is produced from morphine. It is a white fluffy powder and twice as strong as morphine.

In the nineteenth century, opiates were a 'cure for all', and you could buy them from shops without a prescription.

How does heroin work?

Heroin has to get into the bloodstream to have an effect. This is usually achieved by sniffing it, smoking it or injecting it. It is not well absorbed when taken by mouth.

Why do people take heroin?

Given its bad press, you might well wonder why anyone would want to take the stuff. The reason is because of the 'high' it gives. It makes you feel great, much more so than other opiates, and without feeling sick. The problem is that the good feelings are soon outweighed by the side-effects.

Street heroin is sometimes contaminated with impurities and you can get dangerous reactions to these.

What are the effects of heroin?

One effect is that the more you use the drug, the more you need to get the same effect. The other big problem is that you get severe withdrawal symptoms when you stop taking it. These include sweats, stomach cramps, diarrhoea, muscle spasms, painful joints, a runny nose, vomiting, and a feeling of permanent 'flu. These effects start eight to twelve hours after the last 'fix'. Some people suffer from constipation and girls miss periods.

Heroin users are also more susceptible to infections. If you inject heroin and share needles with other people, you are at risk of contracting both hepatitis and AIDS. Overdose, whether accidental or deliberate, can lead to unconsciousness and death.

Medical cover in Europe

E111 is a certificate which allows you to get free treatment in certain countries. It is useful mainly in Europe, and is a must for the EEC countries. It is available from all post offices. Take your National Insurance number with you when you fill in the form. (Lost it? It's a plastic card sent to you when you reach 16.)

The E111 does not cover all medical expenses, and in many EEC countries you have to have additional insurance. If you're travelling outside the EEC, make sure you have private medical insurance - especially for the USA where you may get landed with horrendous bills.

I knew all about travelling and would look after her (a sort of new age Jack Kerouac – you remember you lent me *On the Road* last year?). She seemed to depend on me and always agreed with my decisions. I think she'd have robbed a bank if I'd asked her to. It was bloody ridiculous and got up all our noses.

We went on next to Vienna. Arrived in the evening in a downpour, so bought standing tickets at the National State Opera House for a Wagner concert. It was great to get out of the wet and only cost us about 70p each. Because the place wasn't full, we ended up having seats near the stage with a really good view. It seems a lot of travelling involves having good fortune like this, but it sure was strange going from a pop concert one night to Wagner the next. Not that there was actually all that much difference between them. The Wagner was a bit slower but just as noisy.

The rain had stopped when we came out, and we spent that night in a park – though the girls said they'd never do it again. Vienna parks are the dodgiest in Europe, and packed with heroin addicts. All four of us slept in a bush and we kept seeing people going in and out of this other bush not far away. Eventually I went in there too and there were all these syringes and needles and all sorts of equipment lying around. Gross. We didn't sleep much as there was this other guy just walking up and down. He was on a path that we could see, although we were trying to hide behind some trees. At one end of the path there was an exit on to the street, and he'd disappear out of it for a few minutes and then come back and disappear behind a bush for a bit at the other end. He did that for three hours. Eventually he stopped right in the middle under a lamp post, leant back against it, yanked down his pants and had a massive great . . . .

□ □ □

The page ended there and Jim was only a little the wiser. Relief swept over him — his sensibilities regarding Jane were still intact. He counted the page numbers. This guy was nuts, where was the rest of the stuff? He couldn't have stopped there, for Christ's sake. But he had. There was nothing else in the envelope. Jim's thoughts drifted back to Penny's problems. No — his problems as well, but he was suddenly too tired to care.

FLYING HIGH IN
NASHVILLE
6724 ZC

6 HIGH ON THE BLUES IN NASHVILLE

Jim woke as the bus slammed to a halt in the bus station in Nashville, Frank's letter still clutched in his right hand. He soon discovered that his backpack had been accidentally dumped out of the hold at Knoxville. The bus people called Knoxville and said it would be on the next bus, but that wouldn't be for a few hours. So he walked out of the Greyhound station into a decrepit sleaze joint next door called Mom's Restaurant with boarded-up windows, weeds around the door, and a police car that looked like a permanent fixture parked outside. The smell of food (though not of sweat) was nectar to his nostrils but the live music that had attracted him to the place stopped dead as he walked in. Every guy present had either spent too long under sun-ray lamps or was naturally black, and they were all, every last one of them, looking at him. Faced unexpectedly with the reality of being the only white face in sight, his first reaction was pure fear. As he fled, a large hand swung him round to face the curious stare of a cop from the car. 'Thinking of going in there, were yah?' 'Yes, but I've changed my mind,' said Jim, sounding ridiculously English and a multiple of 100 more confident than he felt. 'How old are yah? And do yah have an ID?' asked the cop aggressively. 'Umh, I'm 19 – and here's my passport . . . ' but shit, he remembered too late that his passport was in his backpack. 'Will my driving licence do?' That at least was in his wallet. The cop sighed heavily, took it, and said, 'English, huh. Well maybe yah don't know, but yah ain't allowed into no bar here till you're 21, so beat it.'

Half an hour later, Jim was walking over rough, uneven slabs of concrete sidewalk, still heaving with indignity and in search of something to eat and a place to stay, when a head appeared from the cab of a passing pick-up and called, 'Where yah from then?' 'England,' Jim yelled back. 'Where yah going?' 'Don't know,' then under his breath, 'and don't fucking well care.' The driver pulled over and another prickle of fear crept up Jim's back. Suddenly the place looked very deserted. But the guy only wanted to ask him what he thought of Nashville, and did he want to see the sights – guaranteeing to drop him back at the Greyhound station later to check out his backpack problems. Well, thought Jim, he might be a mass murderer or as bent as a poker, but it wasn't immediately obvious.

In the cab, with a six-pack aboard, Barry (who was from Tennessee) turned to him. 'Don't suppose I need to ask if you smoke dope?' 'Look at my eyes,' said Jim evasively, wondering what Frank would have come up with in his place. 'Yah, silly question.' Barry pulled out what looked like about a kilo of ganja and rolled a cigar-size joint. It was like a dream, cruising in a pick-up through Johnny Cash's home town, down West End Avenue, through Centennial Park, past a life-size concrete replica of the Parthenon, a Bud in one hand and a joint in the other, with Country blasting on the radio.

Later that night, after more sweet music, drink and

Abortion — some views

- 'I use condoms, but I know they're not 100% safe. Though I don't like the idea of an abortion, if I got pregnant now I'd want an abortion.'
- 'I don't believe in abortion - it's wicked and it's against my religion.'
- 'I think it's wrong to bring an unwanted baby into the world. The world is overpopulated already.'
- 'I think it's no different from murder.'
- 'If nature causes all those miscarriages of babies because there's something wrong with the baby, I can't see why it's wrong for doctors to do the same thing if something is wrong with the baby.'
- 'I don't see why men should be involved in any of the decisions as to whether a woman should have an abortion or not.'

Reminder Most unwanted pregnancies occur at the beginning of a relationship because you don't want to think it's going to happen, or at the end when you think it's all over and it's not going to happen anyway.

Abortion laws vary in different countries

In the UK abortion is legal with the consent of two doctors until the foetus in the uterus is twenty-four weeks old. Deciding whether to have an abortion or not is a difficult decision. There are several options:

- going ahead with an unwanted pregnancy and keeping the baby, or having it adopted
- having an abortion

No one likes the idea of having an abortion, but it is an option and it may be the better of two evils. There are moral arguments for and against. If you find yourself pregnant and decide you might want to have an abortion, it's important to go to a doctor – either your family doctor, a family planning clinic, or one of the private charity abortion clinics – as quickly as possible. The earlier the abortion is performed, the safer it is. It is in any case a very safe operation, and should not interfere with future pregnancies if it is carried out early and properly. In some countries, where abortion is illegal, women can die from having unsafe abortions. They can also get an infection in their pelvis which can make them sterile. If your doctor doesn't approve of abortion, ask to see another one.

In France abortions are legal up until twelve weeks after conception.

In West Germany and Ireland abortion is illegal.

If you decide you want to carry on with the pregnancy, go and talk to a doctor, and make sure you get all the care you need.

What happens when you have an abortion?

RU 486 is a new pill which causes an abortion without an operation. It is best used before eight weeks of pregnancy. It involves taking some tablets, then using a special pessary (a pill you put into your vagina) two days later. Only rarely (1%) is an operation needed as well. This new pill is widely used in France, where 25% of women having early abortions use this method.

Most other abortions (up to twelve weeks) involve having an anaesthetic (you're unconscious while it's being done) and the contents of the womb are sucked out. If you have a later abortion, after twelve weeks, it may be a rather more difficult experience as it is more like having a baby.

After an abortion

Most people have no problems. Some feel sad, even depressed.

The best way to avoid an abortion is to use contraception (and remember emergency contraception).

talk, Barry had cried and confided his troubles. His wife
had left him, taking their daughter with her, and his son
had become epileptic. Barry pulled out a neat stack of
$15,000 worth of hospital bills for the care of his son and
also of his sick mother. They both agreed that socialized
medicine was the only answer – Jim not least because if
Penny was pregnant then abortion was on the cards.
From what he'd heard, private abortions were expensive
– £130 a time – so it would have to be done on the
National Health. This thought overwhelmed him with
self-pity. He had to tell Barry. He'd never meet him again,
he was experienced, and Jim needed to cry too. Barry
listened. 'Yah,' he reflected, 'you've got problems there.
Far as I know, you don't *have* to be inside a girl to get
her pregnant. Lot of kids back home got into trouble not
knowing that. Never had a problem myself – always
use a rubber, whatever I'm doing. I don't reckon with
abortions though, but maybe if I was faced with it I'd
think different.' Funny thing was, thought Jim, although
this guy seemed liberal, vulnerable and sympathetic, he
still believed that the blacks should be picking cotton, all
Jews should be shot, and that Reagan was the best thing
that had ever happened to the States.

Jim's worries eased by booze and food, they collected
his backpack which seemed to have its own travel plans.
Being stoned for the first time and drunk for the 139th,
he couldn't face searching out a local Y. He just needed
to crash, so Barry dropped him off at a motel – the
Olcott at $33 for the night. At this rate, he reckoned
he'd be broke before getting across the States. He'd have
to stick to Ys or Sally's in the future.

Grey with tiredness though he was, the fact that there
were fifty channels on the TV nearly sent him into multiple orgasms. On offer were *Indiana Jones and the Last
Crusade*, *Mississippi Burning*, *Vacation*, and *The Great
Waldo Pepper*, and he was trying to decide between them
when he came across an all-consuming, late-night hard

core sex programme. This really got his adrenalin and testosterone racing and he managed about ten minutes of such excitement before the pressure grew too great and he satisfied his needs and grew bored. Pure sexual excitement one moment, total anticlimax the next. It was the repetitiveness of it all that became tedious. There were only a limited number of things to be shown. All they could do was change the bodies, the bits, the places and some of the acrobatics, putting 'this' into 'that' rather than 'that' into 'this'. The other thing about pornography was that he'd lay a bet that what one person found a sexual turn-on, another person would find a turn-off.

Still hyped up on the sensation of cramming more new experiences into the last seventy-two hours than he'd had in the whole of his life, he discovered a local shop, still open at 4 a.m., selling crisps, drinks, rolling tobacco and a T-shirt saying 'Don't Drink The Water Here – Fish Fuck In It'. He'd either be dead, or a sex maniac with lung cancer, by the end of the trip with this kind of stimulus availability. He couldn't go on at this pace. What he needed now was to sleep. The journey had been about as pleasant as having sex with a Rottweiler, and he had to crash, he must crash, cra. ., c . . . .

Bang! The maid flung the door open on his naked sprawling body, took a long calm look, murmured something sympathetic to herself, and walked out again, deftly dropping the 'Do not disturb' sign on the outside door knob. Rolling over much later, through the sleep-hazed yellow crunch of stuck-together eyelids, Jim saw from his watch that it was 2.23 in the afternoon. He went back to sleep and woke at 7, sixteen and a half hours later. Sitting there in bed he reread Frank's letter and found the missing pages stuck to the back of the last one he'd read. Gingerly he peeled them off and read on.

□ □ □

Contraception

There's no ideal method of contraception. They've all got their pros and cons. What's certain is that you're very likely to get pregnant/get someone pregnant if you decide to take a chance.

How likely are you to get pregnant without contraception?

• If you have sex at the time when an egg is released (about fourteen days before a period), there's 30% risk of getting pregnant.
• If you have sex somewhere around the middle of the cycle (when the egg is normally released), there is still a 20% risk of getting pregnant.
• At other times, the risk is anything from 0-10%.

Most people don't know when they ovulate and although the egg doesn't hang about waiting to get fertilized (twelve to twenty-four hours), the sperm hang around for several days. So even if the egg isn't released for a few days after having unprotected sexual intercourse, there may still be some hungry sperm waiting.

How do you choose which contraceptive?

The important thing is to find out all about the different methods available, and then you and your partner can decide which method is best for your relationship and go for it. You both need to feel 'happy' and safe with the method you are using. What's right for one couple is not necessarily right for another. If, after a while, you decide you don't like what you're using, you can always change your mind and try something different.

What can happen . . .

She thought it was wrong to have sex before marriage. One night her parents were out and one thing led to another. He respected her views, but they both lost control. He meant to withdraw, but he didn't. He thought she should have been on the pill, but she wasn't. She thought he should have used a condom, but he didn't. She should have gone for emergency contraception, but she didn't. They should have talked about it, but they couldn't. She thought she was going to have a baby, but she wasn't. They shouldn't have been so lucky, but they were.

In one study, 70% of couples had had unprotected sex the first time. You may get away with it once, *but don't count on it.*

The choice

You can choose between condoms, the combined pill, the progesterone-only pill, an IUD (coil), a diaphragm (cap), spermicides, the 'safe' period, the contraceptive sponge or withdrawal. It sounds like a lot of choice, but it's less than it seems, as many of the methods aren't very effective.

. . . wank. I'll leave the details to your imagination (and knowing you, you won't have any difficulty). He stayed there for hours till someone else walked by and he was forced to cover himself up. This got us very tense and nervy. As it was, we always went to sleep in our clothes, and I kept my money belt, penknife and wallet under my sleeping bag. We left the rucksacks in a locker at the train station, but kept our important stuff with us all the time as we'd heard reports that lockers were being broken into.

At the end of our time in Vienna we split up as we had different itineraries from there on. Michael was joining his family in Tuscany for a while. The girls were set on going to Greece and then grape-picking in France, but I'd had so many good reports on Czechoslovakia, I wanted to go straight to Prague. I was excited about travelling by myself, freedom and total selfishness – great. A group of four is too many, no matter who they are. Decisions take too long when you have to take so many different interests into account. It's just one bloody great compromise, and you don't meet so many new people either. I reckon the best combination is two, and I'd travel with a bloke next time, unless it was with a definite girlfriend.

I knew I could afford Prague as the exchange rate was still good. I stayed just out of town at a place called Djavik. There didn't seem to be any real poverty – no tramps or beggars or anything – but there wasn't much to buy either. The shops could manage soap, shampoo, food and drinks, but not much more, though the free market was beginning to open up. The city's got some terrific architecture. My only problem was the language barrier which made me feel a bit isolated and lonely till I met up with a friendly bunch of Americans. They made a nice change from my three previous companions. Not that there was anything particularly wrong with them, but travelling is about new experiences and new people.

We ate out a lot and had real pig-ups on dumplings and potatoes with gravy and beef. The choice was a bit limited. They had these huge menus and we'd try and ask what there was, and they'd point to things and say, 'Today, only this and this.' We washed it all down with litres of unbelievably cheap beer.

While we were in Prague, we got hassled a lot by black marketeers, mainly dealing in hard currency – dollars and Deutschmarks being the most sought after. Pounds were just OK. People walked by you everywhere, without stopping, saying, ' . . . want to change money?' out of the corners of their mouths. You had to be careful though as they tried to do you down all the time. You'd be given a whole pile of koruna notes and half of them would later turn out to be cut pieces of newspaper. They used a lot of those tricks. They also had incredibly cheap Levi jeans. I thought about setting up a little business and bringing them back to England to sell.

After that I travelled through Italy – Venice, Pisa, Florence, Rome – all a blur of gelati, pasta and palazzas. Inter-railing was great but my one attempt at hitch hiking, near Rome, scared bits of my body stiff. I was offered a lift by this golden oldie guy and his Barbie-doll wife in an incredibly swish Alpha Romeo. I couldn't understand why we seemed to be taking such a time, with them having this heavy argument in front. Then the guy stops the car, turns round to me in the back, and says in a very heavy Italian accent, 'Please. You have such a beautiful body. We wish you to come to our villa and I watch you make love with my wife.' At first, I didn't think I'd heard right and like a fool I said, '*Per piacere?*' 'We wish you to make love with my wife.' 'What? No, Christ – I just wanted a lift to the station, thanks. Will you take me or do I have to walk?' 'We take you. It *ees* OK. We just want fun, you understand?' I sat in dead silence with my hands between my legs all the way.

Michael was crashed out on the floor of Rome station by the ticket office, just where we said we would meet. It made me laugh – he's always sleeping – but I didn't laugh for long. He'd had his inter-rail ticket, his traveller's cheques and £30 in cash all stolen. The previous night he'd slept in the Coliseum. There were no guards, so he and some others had climbed over the gates and hidden themselves away where they weren't obvious. Next morning Michael found he'd lost his baggage reclaim ticket. He had to get his passport out of his wallet to show proof of who he was, and he left his wallet with his ticket and his money by his luggage. Next time he looked it had gone.

The result was we had to jump the trains home. We took the night train out of Rome and found a compartment which was packed with backpackers, including, amazingly, one of the Americans from Prague. Michael slept underneath the seats, and I lay on top of him drinking wine with the others while he was squashed up below in a black hole of Calcutta.

One final disaster when I got home was that I found my mum had let our cat crap in the roots of my 'pot' plants. I'd left them in the care of my sister, telling her they were lupins. I informed Mum I found this most upsetting as I was planning to study their reproductive cycle.

Well, that's it, I guess. Write soon and tell us all about your travels – Frank

PS What was up with your dear Penny before she left? Everyone says she seemed in a state – but no one knows why.
PPS Jane told me to send her love and ask how you're getting on?

☐ ☐ ☐

How good is your knowledge about contraception?

Test yourself on the following 16 easy questions. (Answers on page 92.)

1. Do you need to have intercourse to get pregnant?
2. Can the woman get pregnant if she doesn't have an orgasm?
3. Can you get pregnant if you don't both 'come' together?
4. Is withdrawal a safe method?
5. Do you need to take the 'morning after' pill within twelve hours of making love?
6. Can the first bit of cum make her pregnant?
7. Can you rely on the 'safe period'?
8. During which days of her period is it 'safe' to make love without contraception?
9. Is the contraceptive sponge a very reliable method?
10. Does the 'pill' help protect you against sexually transmitted diseases including AIDS?
11. Is it OK to use spermicides alone?
12. Are IUDs (coils) a good method of contraception for teenagers?
13. Do condoms help stop you from getting sexually transmitted diseases?
14. Can you only have sex by having intercourse?
15. Does the 'pill' make you fat?
16. How long do sperm survive in the vagina?

ANSWERS

1. No – if some of the man's sperm get near the entrance to the woman's vagina, they can swim up it, though this is very unlikely to happen!
2. Yes – female orgasm doesn't, as far as we know, influence whether a woman gets pregnant or not.
3. Yes – neither partner has to 'come' for pregnancy to occur, as the man can leak sperm before he ejaculates.
4. No – often the man doesn't pull out in time, and he may leak some sperm before he does. Remember that just one drop of semen contains enough sperm to populate the whole of New Zealand. Even so, it is better to pull out than not!
5. No – the 'morning after' pill should be called the 'three days after' pill, because it is effective if taken up to seventy–two hours after making love (NOT after missing the last period – please note).
6. Yes – before a man ejaculates, he leaks a bit of semen which may act as a lubricant, but may also contain sperm.
7. No – the 'safe period' is not a very reliable method. It needs to be taught and you need to be able to chart your periods, your temperature and your vaginal mucus.
8. None are 100% safe – but some days are worse than others. If you have a regular 28-day cycle, then days seven to fifteen after the beginning of your period are the worst days.
9. No – it has a 25% failure rate, but it is certainly better than nothing.
10. No – this is the method least likely to protect you against sexually transmitted diseases (even though it's a reliable way not to get pregnant – if you remember to take it, that is!)
11. No – it's not safe to use spermicides alone, but again, if they're the only thing you've got around, they're better than nothing and do help protect against AIDS.
12. No – they are not recommended unless you've

already had a baby. IUDs can lead to an infection of your tubes and make you infertile.

13. Yes – this is absolutely true and is one of their huge advantages.

14. No – one of the best forms of contraception is all the lovely sexy things you can do and have orgasm without actually having intercourse itself.

15. Not taking the pill may make you fatter – if you get pregnant! A small percentage of women may get fatter on the pill, but you can almost always find one that suits you.

16. The average ones among the whole 300 million of them survive for four days, but remember there is a lunatic fringe which may survive for six to seven days. (The egg is more fragile. There is only one, and unless it becomes fertilized, it dies within twelve to twenty-four hours.)

If you didn't score well on this – you shouldn't be scoring at all!

Health care in East Europe

Free health care is available in some countries in Eastern Europe, in others you'll have to pay. Check in *The Traveller's Guide to Health*, published by the Department of Health. Free copies can be obtained by phoning 0800-555-777; or from your doctor or post office.

Frank wrote moderately naffish letters, a bit like himself, thought Jim. He took himself too seriously, or maybe he was bleaked out by all the drugs he used. Later that evening, Jim met up with Barry again (illegally) in a Country and Western bar, got saturated on music, drank some more, avoided getting stoned, and took the Greyhound out again to San Francisco – Penny's lost period still heavily on his mind. Time was short. Las Vegas, the Grand Canyon, Phoenix, Arizona and LA would all have to wait for another trip.

However, it wasn't until the 23rd December, after three self-indulgent days in SF, that he finally (guiltily) wrote his long overdue reply to Penny's bombshell. What the hell was he to say to her? His performance that night six weeks ago might have lost him Penny as a friend, but he couldn't go on pretending it hadn't happened. No message seemed appropriate. 'Having a wonderful time – has it come yet?' 'America is fantastic – could it have been someone else?' He finally settled for a postcard with a picture of the sun rising over the Golden Gate bridge and the words 'Happy Christmas – are you sure?' He had to hold on to a ray of hope and the message was sufficiently ambiguous.

Posting off this missive with an agnostic prayer, plus a 'better late than never' present of a baseball cap to his sister, he caught the 18.25 Qantas plane for the nineteen-hour flight to Australia. It was the 24th December. 'Happy Christmas?' he asked himself.

Poo!

7 ALL'S WELL THAT ENDS WELL . . .

It was the lousiest Christmas Eve Jim had ever spent. He couldn't sleep, the hostesses were perfect bitches – you'd think they were doing you a personal favour by being with you on the plane. The chances of him waking up to a stocking – with or without an air hostess sticking out of the top – were nil; nor was the plastic tray slapped down on to his fold-down table any substitute for the sack of goodies Santa used to leave him.

When they touched down in Sydney at 6.30 a.m. local time on Boxing Day, grey indifferent rain slanted down on the dead concrete as Aussie Customs ever so politely took Jim and his bag apart for nearly an hour. They even made him take his underpants off. Standing there naked, it occurred to him that having escaped such attentions in San Francisco, having his backside interfered with by Customs in Sydney would be too much. His sensitivities were spared however, though it did occur to him that this search was because of the way he looked. He must appear a certain hit with his unwashed body, torn jeans,

Pregnancy tests

How can you get them?

In this country, and in many others too, you can buy pregnancy testing kits over the counter. They are just as reliable (and are probably the same ones) as those used by doctors. It costs around £8 for two tests, but if you can't afford this, or prefer someone else to do it, go to your doctor or local family planning clinic. Some other organizations offer free pregnancy testing, but you ought to be aware that some of these are anti-abortion groups who might put pressure on you to have the baby.

How do they work?

When you are pregnant, the hormones in your body change. The test detects a chemical called HCG in your pee, which changes the colour of other chemicals in the test.

How soon can you use them reliably?

Most of them are reliable *immediately after* a missed period, and some can tell even earlier. Ask your local chemist for more details. If the first test is negative, you still might be pregnant. It may read negative when it's actually positive in up to 20% of tests, so repeat the test a week later (two or three days later if you can't bear the waiting). If it's positive, it's unlikely to be wrong.

If you don't want to be pregnant, take suitable action straightaway, depending on where you are:

• if you want an abortion, the sooner it is done the better. It is safer, both medically and psychologically.
• if you are abroad, you will probably have to pay for an abortion.
• don't go to some back-street abortionist in Delhi. It would be better to wait a few weeks and come home.
• don't leave it till after twelve weeks if possible. Six to eight weeks is best. Better still is contraception.

Note – in the UK, abortion is legal until twenty-four weeks, but in practice, you'll have more difficulty getting one after twelve weeks.

Periods

Irregular periods are very common, especially when travelling, and are rarely a health problem. Too little, too much, too many, too few, or none at all: it has been estimated that 20–40% of women will have some sort of period problems when aged between 17 and 23. The regular 28-day cycle is a myth for many women. It can vary from twenty to thirty days, or even more than that.

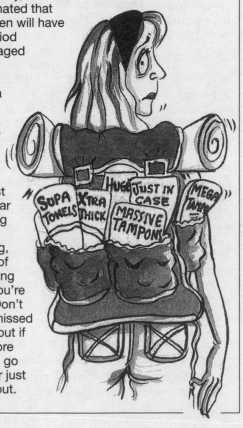

The commonest causes of irregular periods are losing a lot of weight, 'stress', travelling, and taking a lot of exercise (assuming that you know you're not pregnant!). Don't worry if you've missed the odd period, but if it goes on for more than six months, go and see a doctor just to get checked out.

hair long enough to have developed split ends, and a chin with which you could take the paint off a ship's bottom. From now on it would be a clean shave and his best clothes for Customs.

Walking out into Sydney through an internal grey mist of vulnerability, total depression swamped him for the first time. It was Christmas. He was twelve thousand miles from home, totally alone, with nowhere to go, Penny was probably pregnant, and there was no one to talk to about it all. Shit. He couldn't cope any longer.

With hope fading, he summoned up a last glimmer of energy and caught a bus to the train station to cash some money and buy a map. He found that a 470 bus would take him to the Backpackers International, in King's Cross, just down the road from the Hard Rock café. This Backpackers (one of several in the road) had a sign swinging backwards and forwards in the wind. It appeared to be closed – the place was deserted and the door was locked – and he sat down on the doorstep and cried. He probably wasn't the first traveller to do so – or the last.

When the door was finally opened the reception area was packed. Dirty linen bags, bed rolls, sleeping bags, backpacks, canvas bags were strewn everywhere. Jim climbed over the mountain to the reception desk and five minutes later he'd checked in with an unfriendly and harassed lady who demanded 'Your name?', 'Your country?', and informed him it would be $10 a night. Before collapsing in despair on his bed, he crossed the road to the only local phone that worked, in a kiosk littered with syringes and used contraceptives. He had to speak to a voice he recognized, he had to know that home was still there.

'Dad . . . Dad . . . No, I'm fine, thanks. No, everything's just great. No really, it's been fantastic. Happy Christmas!' His emotions were reeling under the impact of home. Beneath all this lay the nagging question he

didn't want answered – but he had to know. And at
more than a tenner for three minutes on reversed charges
he had to find out quickly. His father got there first.
'Mum's been in hospital having a few tests. She's OK,
but it was a bit of a worry for a time. By the way, we
haven't heard anything from Penny. (Oh God, thought
Jim, why did his dad associate Penny with hospital? Was
he trying to tell him something?) He was crying again.
'Dad, is Mum all right?' 'Yes, she's fine now. She's gone
to pick up Gran. But you don't sound too good. Are
things really OK?' 'Yes, Dad. It's so great to be talking
to you. I can't believe that you're not actually here. Will
you give my love to everyone – and especially to Mum,
please?' 'Yes. Ring any time you want to and reverse the
charges again. By the way, you haven't had anything in
the post from universities or polys. Are you sure you
posted the forms? We'll let you know as soon as anything
arrives. Lots of love, son. Bye,' and that was it. Now he
had three worries to cope with. Penny, his future, and
was his mum *really* OK?

Two days later, his spirits fully recovered, Jim decided
that Sydney was rather like London with everyone on
valium – the pace was so much slower. The local station,
however, was pure Times Square, New York – seedy,
dark and noisy, with rust-stained pillars. The 'Sydney
System', as the rail network was known, supported double-
decker trains which whisked him down to Circular Quay
near Sydney Opera House. There, while following a
couple of Australian Sheilas around in a fit of sexual
deprivation, he stumbled upon Alex, of all people, among
the buskers. He would have to have been the worst of
them! There's something really weird about meeting
someone you know from school on the other side of the
world. Funnily enough, Jim found that he got on much
better with Alex in Sydney than he had back home, and
at least he was a familiar face. They talked for three
hours, bobbing across Sydney Harbour past the bridge

to the zoo, half of which seemed to be closed. There were no platypuses and the dingo pen was being rebuilt.

Later in the day, they wandered down to the post office together to see if any magic letters were waiting for them in the poste restante, but it was closed. It was another two weeks (after many adventures in Sydney) before the definitive missive arrived at last from Penny – and from Africa! He took it 'home' to face alone, feeling worse than when his exam results arrived. Gingerly he tore the letter open and began to read.

□ □ □

24th December

Darling Jim – hope you got my postcard in LA? Can't tell you the relief (God, he'd never made it to LA, so he'd missed her postcard) when the pregnancy test turned out to be negative. I wouldn't like to go through that lot again.

The last few weeks have been a fantastic rush. In the midst of all my worries, I was suddenly offered a place on an expedition to Africa which was setting off immediately. Before leaving England, I had to be certain I wasn't pregnant so I did my own pregnancy test. This turned out to be embarrassing as in the first chemist I went into Judith, your sister's best friend, was serving behind the counter. I had to say I was just buying some tampax (I should have been so lucky!). Fortunately the test was negative, but I didn't really believe it till the second test was negative too. You can't begin to imagine how worried I was (can't I hell, thought Jim), especially with no one here to talk to about it. It's just as well I did the test though, because I still haven't had a period. It must be all that stress and now the travelling.

Anyway, enough about that. I want to tell you about Africa. (Thanks for your letter from the airport, by the way.) As you know, I wanted to do something interesting in my year off, and this expedition came up quite by chance through my contacts in forestry. The aim of the group I'm with is to promote scientific research in various countries throughout the world. And what lies behind my expedition is that Tanzanian scientists can't afford to do any field work. Most of them have to have two jobs as it is, so we've come out here to provide the back-up they need. One of the reasons I was so enthusiastic about this expedition was because it is benefiting the country.

When I left the interview in Liverpool that day (when I couldn't come and see you off), I thought I'd be running a high risk of dying out here. I'm not sure whether they were over-emphasizing the dangers – two people actually walked out of the interview – but I was still keen to go. In a way, I think they were laying it on to make sure they got the right kind of people. We had to provide £2,000 each for the first part of the trip, and I had to have another £200 for the Hobo trans-Africa truck to Zimbabwe. When the early place suddenly came up, I was glad I'd already managed to raise the money.

It was great that you'd got my passport for me, but it was a mad dash getting everything else together and having my immunizations. I was nervous about going so far away and not knowing what I was getting myself into. It's a three-month commitment. What really appealed to me though was that I was actually going to a tropical rain forest!

I flew to Dar es Salaam via Egypt, in a slight state of shock after all the recent excitement, and not at all in the mood for meeting the others on the project. When I first saw them, they were all chatting together and I felt really alone. Meeting new people always gives me a kind of sinking feeling in the pit of my stomach. We travelled north, over pot-holes, in the back of a big army truck, and this brought us more together as a group. I felt totally overwhelmed being in Africa at last, and also I wasn't feeling very well. I think I got food poisoning

Emergency Contraception

This is sometimes called the 'morning after' pill, but in fact you have up to three days (seventy-two hours) in which to get hold of it. It's best to take the pills sooner rather than later – though there's no need to wake a doctor up in the middle of the night!

You have to get the pills from a doctor or family planning clinic. You can't buy them over the counter. If there's any chance that you've taken a chance, make sure you get emergency advice. It's much better than needing an abortion or having an unwanted pregnancy.

It's not a method to use regularly, only in emergencies. And if emergencies are happening once a week, it's time you sorted yourself out, as you are only kidding yourself that you are not having sex.

It's very good at stopping you getting pregnant (98% effective), but it's no good at stopping you from getting sexually transmitted diseases.

All you have to do is take two pills with a twelve-hour interval. So don't forget to get it if you forget to use something in the first place.

Another emergency method of contraception is to have an IUD (coil) put in until the next period. This can be done up to five days after unprotected sex.

A lot of people don't know or do anything about emergency contraception. They just behave like ostriches, dig their heads in, and hope it will be OK. In a recent study of women wanting abortions, 70% had known they were at risk of getting pregnant (no contraception or a split condom). If everyone at risk used emergency contraception, at least 100,000 abortions in the UK alone could be avoided.

Water and Disease

• 80% of disease in the world at any one time is water related
• 400,000,000 people suffer from gastro-enteritis at any one time
• half the world's hospital beds are occupied by people with diseases spread via water
• water is related to the: 160,000,000 people suffering from malaria; 30,000,000 people suffering from river blindness; 200,000,000 people suffering from bilharzia

The number of water taps per person in a country is a better indicator of health than the number of hospital beds.

from the aeroplane food, or it may have been just nerves. (Penny's nerves and their effects on her body had a lot to answer for, thought Jim.)

We heard some dreadful horror stories about malaria, and seven out of seventy people who'd been on the project earlier had got it. One had cerebral malaria. She had to be flown home and for a while it was touch and go. So far, except for on the plane, I haven't even had a stomach upset. I've taken my anti-malarial tablets, but I haven't been as careful as some people who've got ill.

The first camp we were in had clean water from a swampy area, but we were worried about paddling around in it because of the danger of bilharzia. This breeds in a snail and gets in through your feet, then eats into your gut and your kidneys. We collected the water in 25-litre cans and then put steritabs (chlorine tablets) into them. In the second camp the water was distinctly smelly and murky and had frog spawn in it. It was actually quite gross. We filtered the water and then used steritabs, but we were worried in that camp because quite a few people in the nearby village had malaria and bilharzia.

Some of the senior Tanzanian scientists are such outright sexists they make you seem *almost* a 'New Man'. (Was this supposed to be a compliment or an insult, wondered Jim?) We were out there in the forest in an overnight camp, three of us, just me and the two biologists – one Tanzanian and one British – and it was taken completely for granted that I'd cook, wash up, and do the fire. This wasn't on my agenda. The English bloke was even more sexist than the Tanzanian. He'd never cooked in his life – it was unbelievable. The boys I knew at school were happy to live in an absolute pit. Their limit as far as cooking was concerned was heating up pot-noodles, and they never bothered to wash up. It used to drive me round the bend and my natural instinct was to do the washing-up and feel resentful. Out here, we're all learning to muck in (even the scientists!).

We get on well with the Tanzanian drivers. They come and sing with us and we all play sport together. The camp is good socially. We were advised before we left to dress like men, and white educated women are treated by Tanzanians as men. No relationships have developed in our group, except for the leader. One bloke was quite keen on a girl but she wasn't interested. When I first met my companions, I thought there's no way I'm going to get involved with this lot (you'll be glad to know!) We aren't sexually harassed either, because we are so well protected in the group. A lot of people have partners back home, though I guess that's never stopped anyone before. It's quite funny when the post arrives. Everyone zooms off to different corners of the camp to read their letters from home, then minutes later we're back together as a group again. It's great to get news from home. You start counting on it, and if you don't hear for a while it's depressing. I hope there'll be another letter from you SOON.

At the second camp, several people got severe diarrhoea and some got this really weird fever which was quite serious. The nurse with us thought they had malaria and gave them quinine. But the quinine must have gone off in the heat or something because everyone started getting high on it. It became difficult to separate the problems of the fever from the effects of the quinine. It was, in fact, relapsing fever rather than malaria. We looked it up in a book of tropical diseases. Under relapsing fever, it said you can have a sore neck, or a sore back, headaches possibly, and possibly a high temperature. Then we looked up malaria and it said exactly the same! It was also at the second camp that we were attacked by ants. We had to run out of our tents in the middle of the night, and got frozen. I never actually wish I could go home, but I definitely miss home comforts.

AIDS

AIDS stands for Acquired Immune Deficiency Syndrome. At the beginning of the 1990s, there were a quarter of a million known cases world wide. The true number was probably nearer a million. But ten million people may now be infected with HIV (Human Immuno-deficiency Virus) – the virus that causes AIDS.

Total of AIDS cases in different countries 1990

	Cases	*Cases per million*
USA	154,791	626
France	9,718	174
Australia	2,295	139
Holland	1,487	101
Germany	5,500	71
UK	3,884	68
Japan	294	2

What causes AIDS?

AIDS is an infectious disease caused by a virus (HIV) which gets into the cells of the body. A person who is infected will carry the virus for life. The virus specifically infects and destroys the cells of the human immune system which normally protect the body against infections and cancers.

How is the virus spread?

(a) By sexual intercourse, in semen and in the fluid of the vagina. It can spread from a man to a woman, or from a woman to a man; and men who are homosexual and have anal intercourse with other men can also spread the infection. AIDS spreads in much the same way as other sexually transmitted diseases (like syphilis, gonorrhoea or herpes) so prostitutes and other people who have many sexual partners are at higher risk of being infected with the virus. You can also get it from oral sex, from either a man or woman who is infected,

but there is much less chance of this than from vaginal sexual intercourse.

(b) From injections – the AIDS virus can be spread by sharing injection equipment. People who inject drugs such as heroin run a serious risk.

(c) Mothers can infect their unborn babies as the virus can get from the mother's blood into the baby's blood during pregnancy.

(d) The virus can be transmitted in blood transfusions or in substances obtained from blood (like those used to treat haemophiliacs). In the UK, this form of transmission is now extremely rare, because all donated blood is tested for the virus. This test is not routine in all countries.

How is the AIDS virus not spread?

You can't get infected by the virus from toilet seats, door knobs, cups, kissing, swimming, or touching someone who has the AIDS virus.

What happens when a person first gets infected with the virus?

The virus multiplies but the infected person goes on feeling and looking perfectly well. It usually takes about three months or more after infection before the blood tests for the virus become positive. At this stage the person is known as being 'AIDS positive' or 'HIV positive' or 'an AIDS carrier' or 'body positive'. The person is infectious and he or she can spread the virus.

What happens next?

As the virus destroys the cells in the body which normally help stop the development of infections and cancers, so the person becomes more and more likely to develop these problems. He or she may also feel tired, develop enlarged glands in the neck, armpits and groin, and sweat a lot. None of these symptoms is unique to someone with AIDS. They can occur in a large number of other illnesses as well. A person with this combination of problems should however see a doctor, and have a blood test to sort out what is wrong.

How do you test for AIDS?

A blood test helps tell whether you have been infected with the HIV virus. It can take at least three months for the test to become positive, so there is no point in being tested the day after you put yourself at risk. You can have a test anonymously at a GU (genito-urinary) clinic attached to a hospital or through a GP.

Does everyone who gets the HIV infection get AIDS?

Probably 'yes' – though it can take anything from a few months up to very many years from the time the person is first infected. A positive test for the HIV virus means that there is a high risk of developing the AIDS disease, though the person may stay well for years. However, infected people can pass the virus on from when they first get infected until they die.

Is there a cure for AIDS?

No. None has been discovered so far – though a drug called AZT is thought to prolong the period between getting infected with the virus and dying from the disease. Other drugs are being developed, including trying to find a vaccine to prevent people at high risk getting the virus in the first place.

We were told before we came out here that 60 per cent
of all Tanzanian men have AIDS. I didn't believe this,
though nobody could tell me the true figure. But one of
the drivers has been having a fling with a local woman
and has boasted that he never uses a condom. It's a
matter of national pride. His lover is only 18 but she has
two children and is divorced. We wondered whether we
should talk to the driver about contraception. In the end,
we decided we couldn't interfere between two consenting
adults in someone else's culture. I've been sharing a tent
with two other girls and a bloke and we talk about
missing our boyfriends and girlfriends, but nothing much
up front about sex, you'll be glad to hear.

My darling Jim, it's Christmas Eve and I'm really missing you. It's funny to think that it's Christmas Day
tomorrow and I'll be going out as usual to collect creepy
crawly things (in my net, I hope, and not in my sleeping
bag). In a couple of days' time, I'm off to Nairobi to
meet up with my Hobo trans-Africa truck for the second
part of my adventures.

All my love — Penny

□   □   □

Christ, I wish I'd got her postcard in LA, thought Jim.
It would have saved a hell of a lot of anguish. Anyway,
she wasn't pregnant after all. (Well, he hadn't really been
worried, had he?) Then another nasty thought crossed
his mind. Maybe he was infertile? What the hell. He had
enough to worry about, with his mum having tests in
hospital and all. He decided he'd ring his father and find
out more. At least he was back in action and functioning
properly again. What's more, it had stopped raining,
there was more of Sydney to see, and then the prospect
of travelling with Alex, instead of by himself.

8 CRACKING UP IN SYDNEY AND SIN IN BYRON BAY

Jim's money was running out. He would have to find a job. But jobs, as Alex, and Jim's fellow travellers at Backpackers International pointed out, were in high demand and low supply. The first drop-off point for money from his parents was still some 3,000 miles north at Darwin. He didn't dare ask his father for a loan of money before then – although he rationalized (somewhat illogically) that he was saving his parents money by not being at home. He managed to pick up a day's casual labour, and then a job at McDonald's. Stinking of burgers as he soon did, he was followed home each day by the entire canine population of North Sydney, licking him over in frenzied delight – the complete opposite of the prostitutes who hung around King's Cross. He'd discovered early on that the hostel was in the red light district of Sydney, but the prostitutes, who were known worldwide to be the fattest and oldest on offer, never bothered with the backpackers.

On New Year's Eve, Jim and Alex were invited to a party on Bondi Beach. The beach was three-quarters of an hour's bus ride out of the city, but was spoilt by being surrounded by regiments of high-rise apartment blocks. Jim had read somewhere that a recent clean-up of the

Pros and cons of one-night stands

For
- make you feel wanted
- make you feel attractive
- they're exciting and give you a buzz
- they're part of a power game which you've won (or have you?)
- sex itself is nice
- there's no commitment
- you don't have to worry about the other person's feelings
- you feel part of the scene because everyone else seems to be doing It
- it might develop into the relationship of a lifetime (should you be so lucky!)

Against
- you might catch something
- you might make someone pregnant
- you might get pregnant
- you might need an abortion
- you might become sterile for life
- waking up next morning with a complete stranger isn't fun
- guilt and shame
- you might give something you've caught to someone you care about
- sex alone, although fun, can be hollow
- if he/she does it so easily with you, how many others has he/she done it with before?

sand here had revealed the odd human body, 234 fridges, 43,178 needles and 56,421 XXXX beer cans. The party was a great free-for-all, with fireworks, jazz bands and barbecues – though the litter and vomit on the sand, in combination with the other debris, didn't exactly add to the delight of it all. Jim got so staggeringly drunk that it was 2 a.m. before he began to realize that the earache that had been there on and off since his flight from the States was searing through his head like a bullet. Alex virtually carried him back to the hostel, dosed him with aspirin, and sat with him, curled up in a chair, until the earache disappeared and he fell asleep.

The next day, Alex announced that his money situation needed drastic action. In a sudden fit of excessive gratitude for Alex's efforts the night before, Jim decided to leave the Backpackers, join up with Alex and camp. The nearest place was half an hour away, and on cue as they descended from the bus, so did the rain. 'It would bloody rain when we decide to camp,' muttered Jim, to no one in particular. 'No problem,' said Alex coolly, spotting a row of rusting caravans for hire. Fifteen dollars lighter (for one night), and by now sodden to the skin, they flung their caravan door open, scanned the room, and saw just one double bed. Jim could have wept. Why had he left the security of the Backpackers? The last thing he wanted was to share a bed with Alex. Penny 'yes', Jane 'yes', Alex 'absolutely not'.

Armchair potatoing the evening away in front of the telly calmed things down a bit, and their relationship remained OK for the next couple of weeks. But one morning, when Jim had to be up early to get to work at McDonald's, Alex, under less pressure than Jim, took his time getting his stuff together. Jim lost his temper, a camera got flung, and Jim ended up sitting on Alex's chest waving a fist threateningly in his face. (The only reason Jim didn't hit him was because Alex looked so terrified.) To make matters worse, Jim got on the wrong train and ended up in Torella on the outskirts of Sydney. He spent a miserable hour waiting for the next train to take him back in the direction of McDonald's. He had never felt so lonely in his life. On the return journey, he met a dreadful girl who talked without drawing breath. She told him her entire life story, her face held twenty centimetres from his (well within the exclusion range of a shy withdrawn Englishman like himself). He hadn't opened his own mouth once. When he finally arrived at work, the manager shouted at him, he shouted back, and he got the sack.

That settled things. They would have to leave Sydney. Jim arranged to meet Alex the following evening at the Greyhound bus station, near the main post office. He was a quarter of an hour late, but there was no Alex. For a while Jim indulged in fantasies of meeting Alex again in Darwin, six weeks later. They'd be like two lost strangers and would recount their different odysseys. As he crouched down in the station bog, a face appeared over the partition wall saying, 'Hi man, what ya doing? Crapping? Don't have a crap man, have some smack.' He opened his fist to reveal the crystals. Jim extracted himself from the cubicle and nearly broke into a run getting to the Interstate bus terminal – the fall-back meeting point with Alex. He was there.

The Backpackers at Byron Bay had a swimming-pool, a washroom, a kitchen, TV, and still cost only $10 a night. It was so full, however, that they had to spend their first night in the TV room. They then got moved to Room 18 with two Germans, Alwf and Bernard – both in their thirties, one a burnt-out doctor and the other a burnt-out architect. It was through them that Jim met Rachel and Cindy, the start of an adolescent dream and a return to childhood. For a whole week the two 22-year-old girls nurtured and cared for Jim as if he had been an innocent puppy, and Jim was only too happy to play the role of a naive and wide-eyed infant.

The 'ons' and 'cons' of condoms

The 'ons'

- 'They're easy to get hold of from chemists, garages, pubs'
- 'They protect me against sexually transmitted diseases'
- 'They help protect me against AIDS'
- 'He has to pay for them'
- 'She has to pay for them'
- 'I don't have to take chemicals all the time'
- 'It's less messy afterwards'
- 'They're easy to carry around and make me feel that there might just be a chance!'
- 'They are very safe and well tested'
- 'I can get her to put it on me so that she knows we're safe'

THIS CAN GROW 600% CAN **YOU**??

The 'cons'

- 'It cuts down on the sensation'
- 'You can't trust a man to use one properly'

- 'I worry all the time that it's going to slip off'
- 'It's like making love with a ski glove on'
- 'It's a passion killer'
- 'He'll think I'm cheap if I carry a condom'
- 'It's like tying the knot and throwing it away makes me feel I'm getting rid of the whole population of America all at one time'

How to use a condom

- Always use a new one – used condoms don't turn a girl on!
- Check the expiry date (but if you're stuck, an out of date one is better than nothing!)
- Take it out of the package carefully – make sure you don't catch your nail on it.
- Put it on your/his penis once it is erect or partially erect – you can't get it on a droopy little thing, so don't try!
- Put it on before any fluid seeps out of your/his penis early on in lovemaking – this fluid might have a few thousand sperm in it.
- Make sure you put the condom on the right way – with the rolled bit on the outside. (It's more difficult than you think. Maybe the manufacturers should have the inside and the outside colour coded?)
- Squeeze the tip of the condom between finger and thumb to expel the air. This makes space for the semen – otherwise it is more likely to burst.

This is what the CLINIC says!

- Keep holding the end and roll it carefully over your/his penis.
- Have sex now!
- After an orgasm, or even if you/she haven't/ hasn't managed it, before the erection disappears completely, hold the condom rim around the penis

during withdrawal to stop it slipping off and spilling all the semen.
• Tie a knot in it, or wrap it in tissue, and flush it down the loo.
• If it floats, wrap it up in some more tissue and try again!
• If that still doesn't work – try the dustbin. Your parents don't always search it!
• If it all goes wrong, and the condom is left inside the vagina after the penis has come out, remove the condom – and if there is any risk that some semen could have spilt, get the 'morning after' pill.

Summary

Condoms are effective – 98% reliable. You can buy them everywhere (well, almost everywhere). They protect you from sexually transmitted diseases, and they don't harm your body in any way. It's true they may reduce the sensation a bit, and interrupt the flow of things while you put them on (though that can be part of the fun). Give them a try!

The 'pill'

Why I like the pill

• 'It's the safest method I know'
• 'I find it doesn't interfere with when we want to make love, as we don't have to stop and fiddle around'
• '... really easy, I only have to remember to take the pill every day and it's done'
• 'After all, they're free from GPs or family planning clinics, and that's what makes the difference for me'
• '... makes my periods not so heavy and always on time, which I like, as it helps knowing when they're going to come'

- '... don't have to worry, it's all her responsibility'
- 'For me, I like being in control of my own body, after all, if something happens, it's me that gets pregnant'
- It's so bloody convenient

Why I don't like the pill

- 'It doesn't protect me against AIDS, or other sexually transmitted diseases'
- 'I keep forgetting to take it, and then I have to use condoms for a week anyway'
- 'I don't like the idea of filling my body up with hormones'
- 'My friend put on weight and had headaches when she was on the pill and I don't want that'
- 'I don't think it's right her having to take those hormone things all the time. Must have some effects, mustn't it?'
- '...I worry about the side-effects'

Summary

The pill is the best contraception for not getting pregnant, as long as you remember to take it, but it's not so good if you want to avoid AIDS and other infections. One option, of course, is to use both. There are some side-effects from the pill, but most women feel fine and don't have any problems.

Possible problems

Minor side-effects These might not sound minor to you, or feel minor when you're suffering from them, but most of them pass off or settle down if you change to a different pill.

- depression
- headaches
- going off sex (the most efficient contraceptive)
- feeling sick
- tender breasts
- moodiness

Most women feel absolutely fine on the pill.

Blood clots and the pill This is *very* rare with the new low-dose pills, especially if you're young, healthy and, best of all, don't SMOKE. Blood clots are still very rare if you do smoke, and it's important not to get pregnant until you really want to.

The pill and cancer There have been lots of scares about this in the last few years. The pill will protect you from cancer of the ovary and cancer of the womb, which is good. Long-term use of the pill (more than five years) when you're young, may result in a slightly increased risk of getting breast and cervical cancer, though not all the studies agree on this.

Remember the pill is the best thing to use if you don't want to get pregnant, and if you use condoms too you should be even safer.

The 'cap'

Why I like the cap
• 'I thought it would be really difficult, but it was just like putting in a tampon'
• '... I like the cap better than the pill. I got fed-up having to take the pill every day. I don't like the idea of taking hormones all the time. They might do something to my body'
• 'The great thing about using it is you don't have to stop and fiddle about in the middle, like with a condom. I put it in before when I know we're going to make love'
• '... means I'm in charge'

Why I don't like the cap
• 'It all sounds really messy to me, and I don't like the idea of putting something inside me'
• 'It's a real bother as it needs to be fitted by a doctor, so you can't just buy it over the counter'
• '... not safe enough for me'

Summary

The cap is a good method if you are motivated and don't mind putting things in and out of yourself. It's 98% effective. It gives you a bit of protection against sexually transmitted diseases, but not as much as a condom.

Less commonly used methods of contraception

The 'minipill'

This is another option if you can't take the combined pill. It's not as effective at stopping you getting pregnant, but in other ways it is similar.

• It's no good if you're scatty and bad at time-keeping, as you have to take it at the same time each day.

• It can cause irregular periods.

This is not the best method for young people. If you want to take the pill, the combined pill is best – unless there's some medical reason for not taking it.

IUD (Intra Uterine Device or coil)

Not recommended for young women who haven't had children. There is a risk of infection of the Fallopian tubes which may stop you getting pregnant later. Only consider this if you can't use anything else.

Spermicides

Don't use them alone, though some spermicide is better than nothing. The stuff does help kill the AIDS virus as well as sperm. It should be used in conjunction with the cap and condoms.

One evening, while Jim was quietly slumbering, they came in and tore the sheet from his bed. Before he realized what was going on, they had taken a polaroid picture of him in his boxer shorts, with a sneak appearance from a pair of gonads. Cindy started to flirt – teasing him, running her hands through his hair, tickling him. He didn't think he could take much more. He didn't want to give in easily (like hell he didn't!). Cindy was the first girl he'd met he could talk laddish to, not worrying about farting and rambling on about the various quirks of bonking.

Rachel, whom Alex was fighting off, was big and ugly and worked in a Swiss bank. She had a permanent expression as if she was having a shit. But Jim fell in love with Cindy. Beautifully slim, with deep dark brown eyes, she was three years older than he was and had an air of slight detachment. A hard one to land, thought Jim, but land her he did.

Evenings were spent together in the courtyard, drinking wine, talking and listening to Latin, blues and reggae. It felt good, everybody was positive, generous, their egos left behind. Often they then went off to a friendly local bar built near a disused railway track. The place was always full, with live music and VBs to drink till midnight, when they went off to the beach for a swim.

The German doctor in their room, Alwf, left and was replaced by a 50-year-old Swedish guy with a droopy face and vast bulbous eyes. What the hell was he doing in a Backpackers, thought Jim, sitting alone in their room all evening drinking vast quantities of wine and lager? Even after the lights were out, Jim could hear him boozing on in the dark. Then he would start to snore, not just on and off, but solidly, with purpose.

One night, Alex got up and smacked him around the head with pillows, then leapt back into bed before the Swede could work out what was going on. It didn't do any good. Alex began throwing coins at him, but it was

Unreliable but widely used methods

The 'natural' or 'rhythm' method

The idea behind this is to find out when you ovulate (about fourteen days before the next period) by a combination of taking your temperature, noting changes in the vaginal mucus, and charting the dates of your periods. It's good in that you get to know the changes occurring in your body, and there are no side-effects (other than pregnancy!). But it's a very unreliable method unless you have regular periods, have been well taught, and are very careful – as sex is limited to 'safe' days, rather than when you feel like it.

'Withdrawal'

The trouble is *it's not very effective* – but if you're going to have sex, it's certainly better than nothing. Much, much safer is to use one of the other methods above.

like kicking an old juke box playing a record with a scratch. It just skipped a couple of notches and then started again. In the morning the Swede was amazed to find himself covered with five-cent pieces stuck to the sweat on his chest. During the day the guy was pathetic, in the small hours he was lethal.

The longer Jim stayed in Byron Bay, the more he loved it. After a week he'd got to know and start caring about individuals at the Backpackers. It felt like a real community, further helped by Ivan, an American, organizing a beach party one night, to which most of Byron Bay turned up, bringing wine, cigarettes and food, and talking and messing around until 2 o'clock in the morning.

That was the night that Jim slept with Cindy. He hadn't intended to. He still wanted Penny, and still felt confused about Jane, but as the night wore on, and the conversation with Cindy grew more intimate, there began to be signs that this was more than amicable friendship. They started to touch one another, and exchange glances of mutual understanding. The touches began to be charged with electricity and could no longer be ignored. At some point during the night, with wine in their blood and with a distant figure outlined against the sea playing blues on a trumpet, there was no going back. Somewhere along the line, his brain told him she'd said she was on the pill, and when he finally came inside her it was the first time and felt as if it would be the only time. It had been too good, too fantastic to be repeated. Perhaps he should just die now, he thought, as he lay there afterwards. Life shouldn't simply go on. But on the way back to the Backpackers, she'd coolly begun to tell him about her boyfriend back home. From the way she talked, she was evidently very much in love with him, and memories of Penny had whirled into his brain. How totally confusing the whole thing was.

9 SURFERS' PARADISE AND FUMBLINGS IN THE DARK

Jim's reply to Frank wasn't burnt off till Darwin, though he'd been writing it more or less all the way from Byron Bay. He hoped Frank was going to keep it for his return. This had been the agreed plan before they left – though Jim was uncertain whether any of them would manage this, especially as his own ability to lose things was increasing by the day.

□ □ □

23rd January

Dear Frank – I've been on the road for nearly two months now. This is the Aussie chapter of my journey. After a great week at Byron Bay (on the west coast of Aussie land) I said farewell to all my new friends and caught the 'backpackers' shuttle' up to Surfers' Paradise. If you stay too long at one Backpackers, the new faces start calling you 'Grandpa'. One friend in particular I was very sorry to say goodbye to – Cindy, who I had a bit

of a thing with – but more of that when I get back.
(Don't tell Jane, and certainly not Penny, please, when
you're next in contact with either of them.)

While travelling up the coast of Australia, you bump
into the same faces and friends. The ones I saw in Sydney,
Townsville, Cairns, and Alice Springs are now in Darwin.
Groups of people tend to move at the same general speed.
Moreover, what I've also noticed about travelling is that
you see faces from back home. For instance, I met up
with Alex in Sydney (do you remember that plonker I
couldn't stand?) and we're travelling together for a bit.
We don't always hit it off, but too long on my own and
I start to need someone to scream at (and beat the hell
out of when I get frustrated). Alex also gives my ego a
boost – me being better looking and all that!

Staying at Backpackers, there's something else I've
noticed about travellers. They're all warm and friendly.
I haven't fallen out with anyone on the road, held a
grudge or felt any resentment – except when I nearly
beat the hell out of Alex in Sydney, but that was different.
If you're with someone for a long time, they can be very
irritating. Like the snorer Alex and I had to share a room
with at Byron Bay. After two sleepless nights, we sneaked
out, walked half a mile down the road and settled on the
beach. Alex had a sleeping bag, I had nothing. My dreams
were horrifically shattered at 3 a.m. when I woke to find
a dog licking my face. I got up to chase it away and the
bloody thing started to play around, jumping up on me
and fetching sticks for me to throw. Eventually it left and
I snatched another couple of hours' sleep and saw the
sun rise around 5. I was surprised how bright it was, and
that there were joggers and even people swimming at
that time of the morning. It almost made me feel guilty
that normally I assigned this great part of the day to
slumber.

It took us two hours to get from Byron Bay north up
to Surfers' Paradise. Along the way, looking out from the

upper deck we could see surfers rising from the watery horizon, rising and then suddenly disappearing into frothy foam. Surfers' Paradise is a *nouveau riche* boom town and made Bondi Beach look as if it needed growth hormones. The place was so big upwards that I needed reminding that twenty years previously it was just a nice beach near a beautiful ocean. Nowadays, it looks as if the sea is merely a man-made swimming pool for one of the grander hotels.

After a week of bliss at Surfers', we caught the Deluxe coach on up to Townsville. The first thing we noticed when we arrived was that people living around the Great Barrier Reef are often missing something – an arm, half an arm, or a leg. I like to think this is the result of shark attacks, crocodiles or wild dogs. For instance, the Alexism for that day was . . . just outside Rockhampton, while waiting for a lift, Alex was approached by a Rottweiler which growled and barked at him. Fearing for his life, Alex lay face down in a ditch for half an hour until the dog eventually lost interest and walked away.

In fact, Townsville has little to offer except a great second-hand record shop and a first-rate hospital, so early next morning we staggered out to catch the *Southern Cross* – a beautiful sleek 1978 America Cup challenger, with a mast that cut through the sky. We sailed out to Magnetic Island. An hour of billowing white above and sparkling blue all around, and we were there.

The island is a tropical paradise. As we stumbled off the boat, I thought I'd stepped on to a film set for Bounty or Cinzano Bianco. We made our way by open-top Beetle from Picnic Bay to Arcaadia, where we booked into a cheap motel and then lay basking in the warm afternoon sun, sipping cocktails, ogling beautiful women, and occasionally floating in the clear Pacific waters. How hard life can be sometimes. We had shark burgers for supper that evening, and wondered how many local limbs had gone into them.

Next day, we met a French fisherman, Roger, who took us on a trail through the rain forest to spot koalas. We saw a couple. They'd remained in the same tree and in the same position since Roger had last seen them, two days before. Do you know that the mentality of a koala is unique? It is perhaps the only animal you could shoot through the head and miss its brain by a metre. Because they are herbivores, they tend to remain in the same eucalyptus tree for most of their lives. And apparently the reason for their lethargy is that eucalyptus contains a drug which makes them constantly stoned. (I sound just like David Attenborough on TV.) Then the koalas get the 'munchies' and the whole thing becomes a vicious circle. Your average koala never stops eating, and it's a miracle they didn't die out years ago. They must stop to have a bonk from time to time, but even for koalas that has its hazards. They have an epidemic of some sexually transmitted disease that humans get too, called chlamydia. Which reminds me, Cindy left me with a present – in the form of a weeping willie. I couldn't believe it. Stupidly I hadn't used a durex. It might have been sticky if I had – ask for durex here and you get sellotape.

□   □   □

In fact, this had given Jim an instant nervous breakdown. The problem had begun with it stinging a bit when he peed. Then he'd noticed a discharge from his prick. It didn't go away, however much he willed it to. As he'd told Frank, he gradually began to be aware that Cindy had left him with rather more than pleasant fading memories. Then he'd become convinced that he had the clap, syphilis and AIDS all rolled into one, and that his willie was about to fall off. He hated Cindy for it, and himself for being so crassly stupid, let alone unfaithful to Penny. After all, sex was not obligatory, even if it was a bloody strong drive – and now he seemed to be faced with death!

It ended with him going to see an embarrassingly up-front Aussie doctor, who'd stuck a swab into the end of his willie and subsequently diagnosed 'non-specific urethritis, mate' – meaning an inflamed pee passage – 'but it's OK, your cock won't drop off yet.' The doctor had given him three weeks' supply of antibiotics, saying, 'No fucking around or boozing while you're taking these, and for fuck's sake, use a franger next time.' He passed the information on to Cindy, as ordered, on a postcard.

◻ ◻ ◻

The doc I saw said it wasn't worth while testing for AIDS yet as it takes at least three months to show up! I don't think I'll ever have sex again. If I don't die from AIDS, maybe I'll be sterile for the rest of my life. Why, oh why, did I dump those condoms in the Virgin's pocket? I suppose I was just too embarrassed to go on carting them around.

Then there was Alex. He had the nerve to accuse me of being too English, and after a heated discussion, he set off to hitch from Townsville up to Cairns while I decided to take the bus. How sweet revenge can be . . . as we pulled out, I sank back into my reclinable luxury seat, directed a stream of conditioned air on to my face, opened a beer, and awaited the start of the 'in bus' video. Then I glanced out of the tinted glass windows and saw Alex on the side of the road, still thumbing a lift in the glare of the midday sun, though he had set off two hours ahead of me. I gave him a brief wave and watched his jaw drop into oblivion.

It was raining at Cairns, so I grabbed my bags and got a minibus to Caranellos 149. I was given a bunk alongside a Japanese guy and crashed out, being careful not to catch my head on the ceiling fan that hovered inches above the top bunk, spinning as fast as a Magimix. But he finally caught his arm in it and ended up in hospital,

Sexually transmitted diseases (STDs)

Sex is usually a nice experience. But it can have a down side like catching a sexually transmitted disease (STD). STDs are a group of diseases caught through sexual intercourse or other sexual behaviour with someone who already has the disease. If you have more than one sexual partner during a lifetime, you might well get an STD at some point. Most of them are caught through vaginal intercourse, anal intercourse or oral sex.

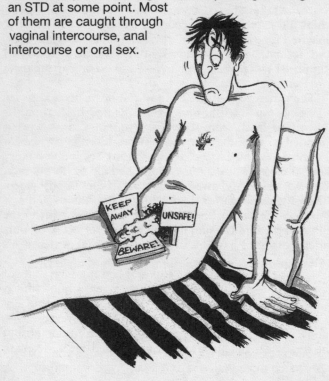

Myths abound when sex is around

Remember:

- You can't catch STDs from toilet seats, doorknobs or towels
- You can catch an STD and not know about it
- Catching some STDs can mean that you won't be able to have babies in the future
- You can still get STDs even if you 'don't go the whole way'

All this will almost certainly not stop you from having sex. It's just a question of taking reasonable care, like not leaping straight into bed with someone you don't know very well. You must show some respect for your body, both because it gives you pleasure now and will give you pleasure in the future.

What are the sexually transmitted diseases (STDs)?

Apart from AIDS, the STDs you ought to know about are chlamydia, gonorrhoea, genital warts, herpes, trichomonas, hepatitis B, syphilis and pubic lice. Other conditions that may be associated with sex, but are not always, are thrush and cystitis. It sounds like a long list and if you're unlucky you may catch more than one at a time. The commonest way an STD shows itself is with a vaginal or penile discharge, some soreness, sores or lumps around your genitals, and/or pain on peeing. If you've had sex with someone and you get any of these symptoms – see a doctor, or go to an STD clinic. Even if you think the person you've had sex with was OK – you never know.

Chlamydia This is one of the commonest STDs nowadays. It is caused by a bacteria. You can only catch it by having sex one way or another. Men may get a discharge from the penis or a burning sensation when peeing. Women often don't know they've caught anything, because they don't get any symptoms. They usually find out because their partner gets symptoms and then the woman goes for a check-up. If you have caught chlamydia, it can be diagnosed by a special swab and/or a blood test. It's easy to treat with a course of antibiotics which you have to take for three weeks. It's worth getting chlamydia diagnosed and treated quickly as it can cause an infection called PID (Pelvic Inflammatory Disease) in a woman's Fallopian tubes and uterus and cause problems which stop her having babies in the future. This is the commonest cause of infertility in women. Men can also get problems from a dose of chlamydia.

Gonorrhoea (also known as the clap) is caused by another bacteria. You can only catch it by having sex. The bacteria can't live outside the body – it likes a nice warm moist place, like the vagina or urethra. You usually get symptoms two days to three weeks after catching the disease. Men get a whitish discharge from the penis and it can sting when they pee. Women can also get a discharge from the vagina and feel pain and burning when they pee, but 90% of women who have gonorrhoea don't know there's anything wrong but can still pass it on to a partner.

If it's not treated, gonorrhoea, like chlamydia, can spread and damage the womb and Fallopian tubes, causing Pelvic Inflammatory Disease (PID). One mild attack and the risk of a blocked tube is 3%, three bad attacks and the risk of a blocked tube is more like 75%, and blocked tubes lead to reduced fertility and even sterility.

Once diagnosed, gonorrhoea is easy to treat with short course of antibiotics. A doctor takes special swabs and looks for the bacteria under a microscope.

> **A Joke** One bacteria to another at an STD clinic: 'I'm a gonna 'ere!

Genital warts There are at least thirty different types of wart viruses. These cause verrucas, warts on your fingers, and warts on all sorts of other places. Genital warts (around your penis or vagina, and even in them when you won't know you've got them) are usually caught during intercourse. They may not appear for three to nine months, or even longer. Depending on where they are, they can be treated with a chemical which is painted on. Otherwise they usually just disappear in time – rather like the warts on your hands and feet. Most types of wart probably don't do much harm, but they don't look nice and you may have caught something else at the same time. STDs like to travel together, and it's thought that certain strains of warts can cause cervical cancer in women many years later. So it's important that if you are sexually active, or ever have been, you have regular, three-yearly, cervical smears. The first cervical smear should be taken two to three years after you start having sexual intercourse.

Herpes is caused by a virus. The commonest kind are cold sores and are not STDs. However, there is a type of herpes that can affect the vagina and vulva in women, and the skin around the penis in men, with blisters and swelling. This is known as genital herpes, and is an STD. As well as the first attack being very sore and uncomfortable, you can get recurrent attacks even if you don't have sex again. And once you've got it, you're liable to infect any other sexual partners.

There are a number of remedies which help the pain, shorten the attacks, and help ward off fresh attacks, but there is no specific cure. There is an old and very true joke about herpes:

Q: What is the difference between love and herpes?
A: Herpes is for ever.

Syphilis is a particularly nasty STD – fortunately now rare. 70% of cases are in homosexual men.

Cystitis means inflammation of the bladder, usually by a bacteria, and/or urethra. It is not always an STD, but it can be. Most women will get cystitis at some time during their lives and it's very unpleasant. Basically it hurts when you pee and goes on hurting when you stop. You pull up your knickers, do up all the buttons on your dungarees, and it suddenly feels as if you want to go again, so off come the clothes and you do, but this time there's not much to show for it and it hurts even more. Sometimes there's blood in your urine.

TOILETS!

Stopping drinking seems the obvious answer to the problem, but in fact that's the worst thing you can do. What helps instead is to drink lots of fluid – two pints straight away, preferably with a teaspoonful of bicarbonate of soda in each pint. This helps flush out the bugs causing the cystitis and changes the acidity of the urine, which helps kill off the bugs. A couple of aspirin and a hot water bottle will help the pain. If it doesn't start to clear up in twenty-four hours, go and see a doctor, as you may need antibiotics and/or a urine test.

Sex can often set off cystitis, but you can get it without sex, and coffee and alcohol can make it worse.

Thrush Again this is not necessarily an STD. You can get vaginal thrush if you've never had sex. About 20% of all women carry the thrush yeast on/in their bodies. It doesn't usually cause problems, but when it does, this is due to an imbalance between the yeast and other bugs in and around the vagina. Thrush makes the vagina and vulva itchy and sore, and there is often a white curdy vaginal discharge. It can also cause redness, itching and soreness in the man's penis. It most commonly occurs after a course of antibiotics (they kill off the other bugs leaving the thrush yeast to multiply); but you can also catch it during sex.

Thrush can be diagnosed by sending a sample of the discharge to the laboratory. It is easy to treat with vaginal pessaries (tablets you put in your vagina) and a cream, both of which can be obtained from the doctor. Men can also use a cream.

Other STDs All in all, there are over twenty infections that can be spread during sex, including trichomonas (which causes a vaginal discharge), hepatitis B (which causes jaundice) and pubic lice (see Chapter 17 under 'Bites').

A short guide to not getting sexually transmitted diseases

- Give up sex, or don't take it up in the first place!
- Don't do it with a stranger.
- Don't pay for It.
- Don't do it with someone with sores.
- Do it with someone you respect and who respects you!
- Feel free to have only one partner.
- Use a condom.

Things may still go wrong, but at least you've tried.

and I think I probably had a couple of free haircuts during my stay there. Alex arrived the next day cursing his luck.

On my second day there, I went into a period of critical depression. It all started when I realized I'd left twenty-four cans of VB on the bus (perhaps I should have hitched after all). Then I had a real PANIC ATTACK.

A panic attack demands some explanation, thought Jim, since it is a phenomenon somewhat familiar to travellers. It is a state of mind that culminates in the revelation that you have absolutely no idea where something you were carrying, of the utmost importance, is. This dramatic revelation is usually swift and enters directly from the subconscious at any time, in any situation and in any place. There you are, casually downing beers, listening to music, and playing pool in the pub when . . . wham! . . . a flash enters the mind, the jaw drops, the eyes spin in their sockets, and a cold sweat pours down your forehead. In one puff you are gone, hysterically sprinting down the road, throwing young children to one side, burning up Porsche turbos, getting to your bag. Throwing aside cameras, clothes, delicate pieces of art you bought for your mum (suddenly these subsidiary objects have no use or meaning), you find – YOUR PASSPORT. Breathing is re-established, underpants are changed, and you can resume a normal existence.

Most panic attacks are thankfully false alarms, but this particular one was different. As well as the beer, I'd lost this vital black bag containing my address book and tickets. I last remembered having it when I'd got off the bus from Townsville – but I also had a vivid and ghastly recollection that the straps on the rucksack were undone. I'd thought nothing of it at the time. Deluxe coaches suddenly seemed a lot less attractive. I trailed off to the coach station for three miserable days, but no bag, and Deluxe claim to have no responsibility for luggage. I had to get replacements for my tickets, which was OK as I had the receipt document in a different pocket. Anything else I could have claimed on my insurance – but what I'd lost was the addresses of people I'd met along the way, including Cindy's!

These problems led to yet another state of mind – the anxiety=inebriation=anxiety syndrome – a sort of vicious circle. The loss of the bag made anxiety take hold of my whole life. To get rid of the anxiety, I got pissed. Having got pissed, I woke up anxious about the loss of my bag and the fact that I was nearly out of money now, and with an almighty hangover. The only solution to this deepening depression was to get pissed again. So most of my nights in Cairns were spent like this – a skinful of booze, go to my room, play catch the bed, then watch it circle twice round the room in the hope of catching it next time around. The bouncers at Magnums got to know me so well they let me in free and bounced me out again free. It soon became a matter of pride among the travellers to see how drunk we could get, until I, for one, started to realize the absurdity of trying to prove my manhood through such profound occupations as playing 'Fuzzy Duck'. This involved a circle of drinkers saying the words 'fuzzy duck' quicker and quicker until one of them said 'does he fuck?' by mistake. The next round was then on them. Not surprisingly, the rounds of drinks began to come faster and faster as the night wore on.

Working a prawn boat out of Cairns appeared to be the absolute answer to my financial problems, but turned out to be a long and harsh saga. The strange thing is, it was also the most exciting of all the things I've done so far. During my time on the boat, every day contained an adventure: hanging off the boom with my feet trailing in the water, trying to grab a rope, with sharks ten metres behind the boat; catching a three-metre hammer-head shark; catching stingrays – as big as a kitchen table – in our nets; catching shovel nose sharks, sea snakes and turtles. Then there was landing literally hundreds of miles from civilization and seeing a doogon, and hunting wild pig through the bush. Every evening as I was starting work, and every morning as the last catch was hauled in, I was rewarded with an outstanding tropical sunset or sunrise over a glassy sea littered with remote islands.

This would all have been fine but for the arguments between me and my skipper, which arose from one simple but total misunderstanding. He'd asked for a 'decky' who'd be a permanent worker on the boat, take over all the scut work and finally skipper it. I thought he knew I was a temporary hand. So he was outraged (justifiably) when he learnt I was a mere backpacker, and I was equally annoyed when he informed me that I was worth only 'food and board' – and no money. You can imagine how keen I was after that! I began to suffer from some quite fundamental unease about my upbringing, education, future plans and grasp on reality. The worst thing was that I was unable to put up any decent defence – he was an ex-cop. Have you ever tried arguing with an ex-cop? Don't – it's not worth it.

It was just me, the skipper and his wife, and I began suffering from another bout of chronic homesickness. It really was a physical pain. The work, although hard, was nothing I couldn't have coped with in a normal atmosphere, but I was picked on for everything. The only solution was for me to get off the boat as soon as possible. Nothing is more demoralizing than knowing that you're not entirely in the right in such a situation. It's easy, looking back, to see that I should have made it clearer who I was and how long I planned to work. I finally got off back at Cairns, with virtually no money.

I was even owed money by Alex, but my chances of seeing that for a while were absolutely nil. In fact, I didn't run into him again until we both got home. I made a 'panic' phone call home about the money that had been promised in Darwin, but no one was in.

Hitching back down to Townsville, I was picked up by a German girl. She thought me totally mad because I unpacked my bag completely twice on the journey to check that my passport was still there, only to discover that I'd left my best pair of Bondi shorts at the Backpackers International in Cairns. I can see them now, the third pair along on the line by the swimming-pool, waiting for a new owner who'll never fill them as well as I did!

Back at the hostel in Townsville, I got to my room in the dark, with visibility around the six bunk-beds almost nil. I vaguely made out a body in the bunk allotted to me, so decided to crash on the bunk below. As I pulled the sheet back and got into bed, I felt something next to me. Someone else was already there. Before I could jump out, the guy had stirred and woken up, so apologizing profusely I clambered out, as quickly as possible, into the pitch black. Cursing that my own bed had been nicked, I felt my way to another bunk, put my hand down to find a mattress, and threw myself on. Suddenly the mattress spoke – it was alive! A guy rose from the sheets with such velocity that he smacked his head on the bunk above. I must have put my hand on his crotch. Backing away to the middle of the room, I accidentally knocked the light on – revealing that my own bunk had been empty all along. I was that pissed.

Next day, I glanced at the noticeboard. My eyes feasted on words which read like a divine sign from heaven: 'Lift to Darwin offered. Meet here at 6 a.m.' I strutted back to my room, whistling Steppenwolf's 'Heading on the Highway', and lay on my bunk in an aura of rekindled faith in mankind.

The following morning, dead on the dot of 6 a.m. I

What do you know about what you are eating?

1. Which food is the most concentrated source of energy?
(a) fat
(b) protein
(c) sugar
(d) alcohol
(e) dietary fibre

2. Which is the most easily available source of food energy?
a) vitamins
b) fat
c) carbohydrate
d) protein

3. If you eat too much meat, what does it get converted to?
a) muscle
b) faeces (shit)
c) fat
d) energy

4. Taking large amounts of vitamin tablets:

a) Can replace meals?
b) Can be dangerous?
c) Is necessary in addition to a good diet?

5. Which of the following does not contain carbohydrate?

a) jam
b) bread
c) milk
d) butter

6. Which of these is not high in fat?

a) lean red meat
b) fruit
c) bread and potatoes
d) cheese
e) none of these

7. Which take-away foods are low in fat?

a) hamburger without chips
b) ham and cheese sandwich
c) fish and chips
d) none of these

8. A good diet should have carbohydrate, protein and fat in the following percentages:

a) 40%, 30%, 30%
b) 75%, 15%, 10%
c) 55-60%, 10-15%, 25-30%
d) 30-40%, 25-35%, 25-45%

Answers

1. a
2. c
3. c
4. b
5. d
6. b and c
7. d
8. c

was there — followed two minutes later by a desperate-looking woman. But no way was I going to offer any gentlemanly bullshit about giving her my place. This was a rat race. It was dog eat dog. The guys providing the lift were called Mat and Crispin, but rapidly became known to me as Dickhead 1 and Dickhead 2. They were sheep farmers from Cumbria who'd been working in Perth for two months and now had two weeks to see the rest of Australia. They were going to Darwin via Alice Springs, but anything west was OK by me. By 7 a.m. we were on our way to Mount Isel in a V8 4.5 litre Ford Falcon, which Mat — even on the straight roads of the vast outback, where traffic was a hypothetical concept — insisted on driving at no more than 60 mph.

One of Dickhead 1 and Dickhead 2's pastimes was waving at passing cars. A car wave in reply was worth one point, a truck wave two, and a toot from a fifty-metre road train was allotted five. Failure of response received two fingers and the yell of 'shitcakes'. Mat and Crispin drove dressed only in their swimming pants to get a suntan. I wish I hadn't bothered to explain that glass cuts out the ultra-violet light, because the dickhead not driving then spent the day with his bum stuck half out of the window. At the end of each day, they did a careful tour of inspection of their rear ends to assess their tans, though to my eyes these remained as pink as the day they were born. A brief squint at the radiator grille at the end of each day (and a good imagination) could recreate the whole of the day's wildlife. Kangaroos, cows, and wallabies were strewn by the roadside — their only epitaph being a Dunlop motif across their foreheads.

The second night we camped an hour's drive short of Three Ways, with me trying to sleep on the less than accommodating bonnet of our car, out of the way of creepy crawlies. It was a sleepless night spent star gazing and listening to the howl of the dingos. We made another 6 a.m. start, taking gas and water aboard (fifty litres of each) on the outskirts of town. The only significant landmark around there is a sign saying to Adelaide, to Darwin and to Townsville, the three arms pointing in different directions.

Time to sign off. Best wishes from your travel-weary friend – Jim

PS   Please don't lose this letter.
PPS   *Please* don't lose this letter.

10 SEX AND SUN IN SIROS, PAROS AND NAXOS

In Darwin post office, another letter lay waiting for Jim – from someone who'd played little part in his thoughts of late. The letter (which had originally come from the YWCA, 11 America Street, Athens) had travelled several times around the world to reach him – judging by the number of postmarks. Careful analysis of these showed it to have been posted in September, and then it had been forwarded to him in Darwin by surface mail via San Francisco, the Philippines and Sydney. Such are the wonders of the modern postal system – but she *had* remembered him, and Penny was right about how good it is to get letters (though this reminded him how few he'd written himself).

□ □ □

12th September

Dear Jim – As promised, a letter at last, though I'm sure Frank was frank about our epic when he got back! I hope you got the PCs. I was sorry to say goodbye to you in Wales. We had a good time, didn't we? (I hope Penny's OK in Africa, by the way?!)

We were full of expectations when we caught that late-night boat from Harwich to the Hook of Holland. We couldn't find seats, so woke up an ancient couple, each lying across three. This resulted in a full-scale feud involving all the neighbouring passengers. We won eventually – only to find that the seats were a lot more uncomfortable than the floor. We had to sit there on a point of principle for the whole way, while the ousted Dutch pair scowled at us whenever we moved.

I bet Frank told you about the 'live sex' show in Amsterdam. If he said Kate and I enjoyed it, he's a lying hound – or just totally insensitive about other people's feelings (which he is). The whole thing was obscene and the place was packed with dirty old men. We were the only women there, they must have thought we were perverts. To tell you the truth, Kate and Frank had a hate/hate relationship from the start. Just as well we parted in Vienna, as they were on the verge of killing one another.

We arrived here yesterday (Kate and me, that is, in case you think I've taken up with some MAN), and we're staying in the local Y. I'm too exhausted to write any more in detail, so here's some scribbles from my diary. They're a bit unedited but I thought they might amuse (and I've got permission from Kate to include her bits too. Mind you distinguish between her bits and mine!) I miss you – but as you'll see from the enclosed bits and pieces, I can't complain about not having a great time.

With love – Jane

1st September I'm writing on a ferry on the way to Siros – very choppy sea, very high wind. The waves are crashing over the bows and people are puking up in the toilets. Me and Kate are sitting in my sleeping bag on deck, reading a letter from David (collected poste restante in Athens), saying he and John will meet us in Languedoc

The sun

Who needs to worry and why?

Everyone needs to watch their skin and protect it from sunburn. You need to take special care if you have:
• fair or freckled skin that doesn't tan easily, or burns before it tans
• red or fair hair and light-coloured eyes
• very moley skin
• had a previous malignant melanoma, or if someone in the family has

How can you look after your skin?

Your skin is there to protect you from all sorts of things like cold, heat, sun rays, infections. It is worth looking after. So here are a few handy tips:

• **tan gradually** as it usually takes three or four days for the pigment which gives you your tan to develop. Build up the time you spend in the sun slowly. Start with ten minutes and increase gradually. Never stay in the sun until your skin goes red. The damage will already have been done. Don't sunbathe for long periods in the same position. Build up exposure in the early morning and late afternoon, when the sun is weaker.

• **there are good protective creams** nowadays which absorb or block out the sun's harmful rays. Although they have numbers indicating their 'strength' – the higher the number the more protective the cream – different manufacturers use different standards. *And remember* sun blocks do not prevent all the sun's damage.

• **avoid the sun** during the middle of the day. Early morning and late evening sun are probably OK, however hot it is.

• **remember** that in the middle of the day, you can get badly burnt even if it doesn't feel very hot.

• **remember** that you can get very sunburnt on a sunny day in a freezing climate in snow, because of the sun and the reflection off the snow.

• **especially sensitive areas** are lips, eyelids, nose, cheeks, upper chest, shoulders, nipples, top of the feet, soles of the feet. Keep these areas well covered, or if you must expose them, do so for short periods using a screen cream of 10 or more to begin with.

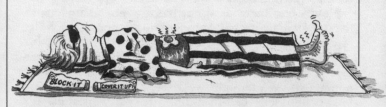

What are the long-term problems with sunburning?

• an increased risk of developing malignant melanoma, which is a skin cancer and probably related to severe sunburn. However, it is clear that there are other reasons for it which aren't yet fully understood.

• the danger of developing rodent ulcers, a skin cancer usually occurring on the face of older people who have been exposed to a great deal of sunlight over the years (Australian sheep farmers, for example).

• damage to the skin which adds up over the years. Contrary to popular belief, the sun is not necessarily good for your skin. Over long periods of time, too much sun can turn it horny and wrinkled.

What about sunstroke?

This can develop if you overdo sunbathing in a big way. The signs include blinding headaches and vomiting. It can be avoided by taking the precautions outlined above and by making sure that your head is in shadow, by either wearing a hat or staying out of the sun altogether. Children are more liable to sunstroke than adults.

in a couple of weeks' time, to go grape-picking. I think we might try and get into a lifeboat. More later if we survive.

2nd September Well, here we are on the beach, being battered by the elements. Siros is not very touristy or beautiful, but it's nice – quite windy, no, very windy, no, positively hurricany! I'll have to stop because me and Kate are getting bashed and smattered to pieces.

Now we're lying on a hot balcony in our own posh flat (£3.50 a night), with a fridge and all mod cons! We're in Gallilosos, a half-hour bus journey from the port. It's a grotty sort of town with massive buildings and a few nice restaurants (though it seems they've never heard of houmous!). We thought we'd spend a few days getting brown and sexy before hitting the 'party' islands. It's time for bed, after a 36-hour-day travelling. We're just beginning to recover from the company of Frank and Michael.

3rd September Jellyfish have arrived in the now windless sea, so we are roasting on the beach, turning various shades of beetroot but not daring to cool off in the infested ocean. Kate's terrified the jellyfish will sting her. A rather nice grunting hunk from the steamy disco has just sat down, and we've all got the giggles. Our roving reporter, Kate, has arranged a dodgy pick-up with a slimey DJ at 3 p.m., so we're all disappearing in a minute. In the meantime, she'll give a quick run-down on the nightlife here, about which she's so expert.

GREEK NIGHTLIFE *by Kate*
How can I begin to describe the simmering melting pot that is Siros's nightlife? The flashing strobes, the pulsating beat, the greasy Greeks, the deafening music. My DJ effortlessly mixes one foot-stomper with another, while never lifting his eyes from the glamorous clientele, his

fingers snapping unconsciously (and out of sync) to the pulsating rhythm. Popular tunes from the last fifty years blare out, the punters mouthing the words as they sip their colourful cocktails. This is surely the heart of 'romance city', where casual affairs begin and end in the blink of an eye or the winkle of a stiletto heel. Glances are exchanged across the crowded floor, and assignations are made to meet on the beach at 3 o'clock next day. Now I'll hand you back to our Greek correspondent.

After such journalistic style, what can I say, except that the disco was practically empty – just a few desperate men whose only asset was that they were willing to buy us drinks. Tonight we're going to save money and sleep on the beach, but first it's off to the bar for an ouzo.

4th September Tonight we're setting out for Paros. Yesterday evening we walked up to a little church on the cliff and watched the sun set. Then we went on to the Banana Night Club where we all got pissed and danced, and then went for a midnight swim with two Dutch blokes – one of them very . . . (Jim noted with dismay that a word had been heavily crossed out.) Don't know whether swimming after drinking is a terribly good idea.

Sleeping on the beach last night was an odd experience. (Bloody hell, had she been up to the same as he had, Jim wondered? If so, she wasn't telling – any more than he would.) There were loads of other people we tripped over, but finally we found a nice spot. At this point an old hunchbacked man on crutches and a Greek woman came stumbling over to tell us that it's their tree for making love and pissing under!! We moved on pretty smartish, and finally had a good night's sleep, interrupted only by a minor hurricane, some nasty nibbling insects, my sleeping-bag zip breaking, and the noisiest birds you've ever heard singing a dawn chorus.

We spent today on a pebbly nudist beach, with a man

The rise and rise of the penis

Most frogs, toads and newts go in for safe sex, so although the sexes get close, there is no actual penetration. The male just scatters his sperm in the water as the female lays her eggs and hopes that it will hit the mark. The 'penetrative' penis came in with reptiles, some of them even being lucky enough to have a double one, forming a groove for the sperm to slide down. These tended to point backwards. Birds can do it during flight! Most legged animals have penises which point towards their head and are attached to their stomachs by a kind of sling. Some rodents and marsupials have the added attraction of a penis with a curve in the middle. As animals evolved and began standing up on two legs, the connection between the penis and the abdomen was lost. The penis began to wave freely in the wind, as in man.

Alice (in Wonderland) might have got a shock comparing the Walrus and the Carpenter because whereas the Carpenter might have been a relatively well-hung 17 cms the mighty walrus can stretch to 60 cms.

HUGE!

Some animals even have a bone in their penis, an evolutionary trait which some women will be relieved to hear has been lost. The purpose of the bone seemed to be to help the poor old male animal when he had to keep his erection up for long periods of time.

Other animal species go in for spines, lappets, frills, and all sorts of other natural attachments which appear to help attract a female. Sometimes the spines also act as 'locks' for those animal couples who want or need to do it for a long time. The trouble is that this makes them rather vulnerable to attack from predators while on the job.

Man, when attracting the female of his species, has to make do with having the largest primate penis. This he can, should he want to, make even more attractive by adorning it with rubber ware of every colour of the rainbow and with every kind of attachment under the sun. For sexual attraction, he also uses his bodily hair and pheromones. Man's one disadvantage compared with other primates is that he has comparatively small testes and a low sperm count, though 300,000,000 sperm per ejaculation might seem more than adequate for a single egg.

Average Size Ranges for the Unerect Penis at Various Ages

10 years	4 to 8 cms
12 years	5 to 10 cms
14 years	6 to 14 cms
16 years	10 to 15 cms
18 years	11 to 17 cms

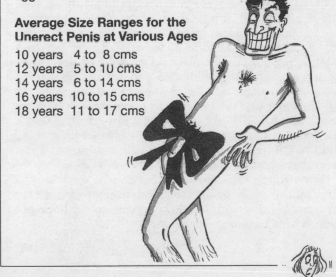

with no willie (apart from the teeniest stump), who spent the day standing next to me and Kate. Meanwhile, Kate has been trying to write a poem.

ODE TO A PEBBLY NUDIST BEACH
It's not very comfortable to sit with stones stuck up
  your bum,
and pebbles which shave your toes whenever you walk
  or run.
Yet the sea is turquoise, the sky is blue
  and the waves coldly caress you.
There's a certain satisfaction in the pain of the sun
  which should be soaked up while you're free and
  young.
And if you haven't got a willy
Then you look very silly
Standing in the nude.
You can't do anything rude . . .
Can you?

Good – isn't it?

5th September We arrived in Paros last night, after travelling in a boat full of mad Australians. (You're probably quite familiar with this breed by now!) We were bundled into another boat as soon as we arrived, and got to a campsite at 3 a.m. The place where we had decided to sleep was completely unshaded and I woke up boiling hot in blazing sunshine. 'Feel like a hot chilli pepper in the blistering sun' . . . pretentious quote from Bob Dylan song. The island looks great, with lots of little Greek alley-ways and lots to explore. My camera won't work, and I've got half the beach in my belly button, but apart from that, I'm very happy.

Here's Kate's summing-up of her holiday for you – so far. Can this really be the nice, well-brought-up girl I set off from London with, all those moons ago? I hope her parents aren't going to blame me!

KATE'S GREEK HOLIDAY

Day – arrived and got a tan, ready for action.

Night – we hit the disco and wonder if anything will happen. Hope so! Spotted a nice German. Turned out to be Dutch, but I'm not known for being fussy.

Late night – I suggest skinny dipping. Ideal opportunity for a bit of nooky – know what I mean? Discover he has a nice body. Lucky I prefer them podgy.

Boy, could he kiss!

Intelligence – 0 – not important

Face – 3 – could do with a shave

Swimming pants – ? – none needed

Bodily hair – 0 – bald as a flaming coot

Friskiness – 9 – but almost *too* eager

Smell – 2 – a bit strong on the sweat aroma

Lips – rubbery but firm

Tongue – WOW could it move!

ONE-EYED SNAKE – (most important) – hung like a snail!

6th September Altogether a hectic, drunken night.

7th September On Antiparos now, staying in a little chalet for £2 a night, having a recuperative period after getting very drunk and having very little sleep on Paros. There's a nice breeze and we've just hired lilos. Tomorrow we're going to explore the island and maybe sleep on the beach somewhere, and then it's back to Paros for a night or so.

FROM ROVING REPORTER KATE

Back once again in our campsite on Paros, enjoying the warmth of the sun and the luxury of rush matting cradling our every limb. We're having a quiet relaxing Sunday stretched out upon golden sands, with crystal clear waters lapping our toes – and occasionally stretching further to envelop our towels and other possessions. The view, ah, the view. The greenery of the scenery, the brightness of

More boozy stuff

Why people drink:

- Relaxing
- Nice feeling
- Makes me hard
- Makes me feel sexy
- Makes me feel happy
- Makes food taste better
- Gives me self-confidence
- Makes me forget my troubles
- Helps me get on with other people
- Other people are doing it so I should too
- Something to go with the cigarettes that I smoke

Words for being drunk

There are fifty words for being drunk in the English language. See how many you can think of. Here are some starters: sloshed, pissed, Brahms and Liszt, blind, mellow, sozzled.

What does 'proof' mean?

In the eighteenth century it was decided that some standards for alcohol were necessary so that people knew what they were getting when they bought a bottle of spirits. The solution of water and alcohol was 'proved' against a standard measure of gunpowder. Water was added to 100% alcohol until the mixture wouldn't ignite the gunpowder. This happened at 57% pure ethanol, which is 100 proof. Most bottles of gin, brandy and whisky are 70% proof, or 70% of a 57% solution, or equal to 40% strength of ethanol. Calculations are different in different countries. In the UK, the percentage of ethanol is approximately half the proof on the label.

Alcohol and calories

Alcohol gives you lots of calories but not much else except a hangover. Some calorie contents:

• one unit of ethanol contains 60 calories but a sweet wine might have 250 calories per unit
• a bottle of 70 proof whisky has 1,800 calories
• a pint of beer has 180 calories

Drinking fantastic amounts of alcohol tends to make you eat less, but drinkers often put on weight because they drink so many calories. After drinking alcohol, most of the ethanol gets absorbed in the first part of the intestines and is transported to the liver in the bloodstream where it gets converted into fat.

Sex and alcohol

Alcohol can make you randy. 'Great,' you say – BUT, alas you then find you can't get it up, and even if you do manage that poor old drunken erection, coming takes much longer or doesn't happen at all.

the whiteness, the glitter and the shimmer – marred only by a huge industrial oil rig just three metres off-shore.

From the beach, straight into the showers for a freshen-up. Did I say straight? Only an hour and a half in the queue for the pleasure of having luke-warm salty water dribble and trickle down my back. The follow-up is a trip to the ultimate in insanitary experiences – a shit in the squatters. I feel every muscle strain as I crouch over the hole, feet planted firmly on the perfectly shaped foot-rests on either side, hands grasping fruitlessly at the shiny tiles, looking for a hand-hold but failing to find one. The one drawback about camping holidays is the loos. I'm becoming conveniently constipated to avoid having to use them very often!

9th September It's dusk. We're about to tuck into two bottles of rum (about £1 each) and some coke (our attempt to be healthy), then it's off to town. There's a rather sexy man parading up and down in front of us, in a flash pair of fluorescent yellow briefs. Kate's pissing herself with laughter.

We've just been on a hilarious bus tour to a beautiful butterfly valley with an awful tour guide. We went on to visit a nunnery, where Kate had to be given a sleeping-bag skirt to make her decent. One more night here and then we're definitely moving on. We were planning to leave today, but didn't – no energy.

10th September We're staying in a place on Naxos called the Mimikos Rooms, with this crazy manager who keeps saying, 'Pliss mees, Mimikos Rooms is for *quiet*. Pliss, pliss mees, shut the door slowly, and remember proper place for toilet paper is in the BIN. Pliss mees, turn the lights off, mees, mees, do it pliss. You leave light on in bathroom. Notice say, "Turn lights *off*".'

11th September This is ridiculous. We are back at the campsite on the beach at Paros, soaking up the sun and discussing what booze we should buy before going off to the disco. I love it here. When I stepped off the ferry, I felt like I was coming home, bumping into people I knew and others I recognized — like the dick-headed watermelon seller. I bought myself a new bikini on Naxos, from one of the tripped-out sellers (less of a rip-off artist than the usual ones though — it only cost 2,000 dracs, about £6), so now parts of my bright white bum are just asking to be burnt. Naxos is basically hippy land, full of fairly boring nightclubs playing Led Zep and Pink Floyd all night. Everyone is too mellow to have good, raucous, football-hooligan style piss-ups.

12th September Everything has gone wrong. I missed the last boat back to the campsite last night, after drinking too many tequila slammers out of plastic cups, plus things called 'Zurmays' (very dodgy shorts with about 90 per cent serious meths in them). I slept in this apartment, and when I tried to catch a boat this morning, there was loads of hassle but I finally made it back. By the time I'd packed, all the boats back to Paros had been cancelled because of the wind. There were five of us, complete with hangovers, in the midday sun, having to trek two miles into town with massive rucksacks. We then discovered that the tickets we'd bought from a dodgy tourist agency for the ferry were for the wrong boat, so we missed it. The guy looking after my sleeping bag was on the right boat — and I didn't even know his surname. We finally ended up on this luxury liner with a swimming pool and a disco and cheaper food than on the campsite — Greek salad and bread and coffee for 300 dracs (about £1). I was in paradise, totally unbelievable. Me and Kate look and feel a mess after our Greek experiences, and need another holiday to recover. Just as well we've got grape-picking to look forward to.

Jim didn't know what to feel. She didn't sound like the
Jane he remembered. She missed him, which was great
for his ego — but it didn't sound as if she'd been exactly
virginal on her trip. But what was that to him? There
had only been a glimmer of something between them —
nothing to pin anything on; and then there was Penny,
to say nothing of Cindy — though she had almost faded
from his mind, if not from elsewhere on his body.

There was a package waiting with Jane's letter. It was
from his sister.

☐ ☐ ☐

London
2 days before 28th January
(my b'day, please note!)

Dearest Bro — humble apols for not having written
before. Thanks very much for the crappy present you
sent me for Christmas, which I'll never use, oops! sorry,
force of habit. Hope you are having an absolute stonker
of a time over there in Aussie land. From your Christmas
note, it sounds like bliss in a nutshell with lots of melted
marshmallows. You are sooooo lucky going round the
world. It's my big ambition — a bit stupid and dim, but
then so is my other ambition — jumping out of a big lump
of metal that flies very high in the sky with a piece of
cloth with a hole in the middle attached to my back. I
won't write for long because everything I say in letters is
complete cow crap. Thought you might enjoy the
enclosed tape instead. That's all the news from your
dinky-do sister. See you when you get skint and come
home. I'm sure Mum and Dad would say hullo, but
they're at the doctor's at the moment. Nothing serious.

Byeeeee — Mary

11 THE EVOLUTION OF DARWIN

The letter from Jane prompted another spell of writing activity.

□ □ □

24th February

Dear Jane — I hope you got my last letter. (This was not the first time Jim had used this subterfuge for not having written. He'd just claim it must have got lost in the post.) In about seventeen hours I leave for Bali. I've just watched my last Australian sunset over the Timor Sea and have decided that Australia has a lot to offer. I don't reckon I'll ever live here, but I'm sure I'll come back. Thanks for your letter. It reached me here after taking part in a trans-globe marathon.

I hope Frank lets you read my letter to him describing some of my trip so far. The choice of what to do now

Sharks

The most feared shark in the world is the Great White, which is usually found off the coast of the USA. Australia does have a shark problem and popular beaches in Australia are protected with 'gill' nets suspended between buoys, parallel to the beach and outside the breaker line. The majority of shark attacks take place in shallow water about one metre in depth and about 100 metres from the shore. Not surprisingly, most attacks occur during daylight hours and most injuries are to the lower limbs and buttocks.

Shark attacks are however *very* rare. Only good common sense about where to swim is needed – rather than fear!

I'm here is essentially between travelling from Darwin up through Indonesia and Malaysia to Bangkok (and from there to India), or going back down to Sydney and flying from there to Bangkok and exploring Thailand. My feelings about this are very mixed. I don't want to rush through one country after another, like a lot of travellers. Some friends I've met out here have given me an itinerary of places to go to that other people don't visit. However, since I feel that I will want to visit all these places again, more extensively and as soon as possible, travelling up through Indonesia could be looked on as an exploratory 'field trip'!

I think my last letter to Frank finished in Three Ways, so I'll bring you speedily up to Darwin. Still with these two dickheads, Mat and Crispin, in a vast great Ford Falcon, I banged down to Alice Springs and the Red Rock. We couldn't come to Aussie land and not see this, even if the detour was 2,000 kms out of our way. It took us two days to get there, and we arrived just as the sinking sun lit the rock up like a huge red-hot coal burning in the middle of a darkening desert. We climbed it at night by the light of a full moon, and we could see to the horizon in all directions. Sitting there at the top felt like being at the axis of the world, and I'm now convinced of the Rock's sacred virtues.

We then beat it up here, killing about ten rabbits every minute or so with a 'thrup' or a 'thud', depending on whether we caught their head or their tail. We camped one night at a picnic site called Katherine Gorge – sleeping on the picnic table surrounded by a thousand kangas – and arrived here expecting the money from my dad to be waiting for me at the Australian New Zealand Bank. It wasn't.

The next two days were among the most anxiety-ridden in my life. I was totally broke and at the far end of the world. Everywhere around me was food I couldn't

Water needs

Water is a vital commodity for human life. A family of six needs over twenty gallons of water a day, just for drinking, cooking and keeping clean. But only one in three of the world's households has a water supply in the home.

The demands on the earth's water resources are growing rapidly, partly as a result of population growth but even more because of industry which now uses huge quantities. It takes 100,000 gallons of water to produce one car. That is thirteen years' supply for a poor Third World family of six.

Is flying a risky business?

Absolutely not. The risk of being killed in an aeroplane crash is 1:10,200,000 per flight. The risk of being killed on a ride in an amusement park is 1:60,000,000 per park visit. These risks are very, very low. If you must know, flying on small Third World airlines is rather more risky than flying on large western airlines, but not much. By comparison – in the UK:

• 0.04 plane passengers are killed per 100,000,000 passenger miles travelled
• 0.15 bus passengers are killed per 100,000,000 passenger miles travelled
• 1.30 car passengers are killed per 100,000,000 passenger miles travelled
• 10 pedal cyclists are killed per 100,000,000 pedal cyclist miles travelled
• 19 motorcyclists are killed per 100,000,000 motorcycle miles travelled

eat, books I couldn't read, cigarettes I couldn't smoke, booze I couldn't drink. I started looking for a job and finally picked one up which turned out really well – cataloguing a whole AIDS file for some researchers for two weeks. It wasn't the sort of thing I thought I'd find in the middle of nowhere. Some of the files made great reading. The answers were so amazingly explicit, I couldn't believe that this was a research project rather than the script for a great blue movie. I suppose it's the only way to get the details, other than observing the action direct.

With this letter, I'm sending you the first photos I took on my really cheap, just bought, camera. Yes, you were absolutely right in Wales when you said I'd need one and I was stupid to think I wouldn't. The first picture is of Red Rock. Is it not beautiful? I'll explain them all to you when I get back, whenever that is! As well as your letter waiting for me in Darwin, there was a tape sent me by Mary with all my favourite songs on it, plus a message from her and Mum and Dad. I nearly cried listening to it.

The pubs here are similar in some ways to those back home, and the one I'm writing this in has a strip show. (Not as 'up-front' as your one in Amsterdam though!) The buildings in Darwin are brick, and every shop, pub and eating place is air-conditioned. In the monsoon season, when the humidity is 96 per cent, the only way to survive is to rush from one air-conditioned building to another. The town is very flat, square and well planned. There's a lovely sandy, shallow beach which is supposed to have sharks, but I didn't see any.

Dad's money, what there was of it, finally turned up, so what with that and the rest that I've earned, I'm moving on to Bali moderately well loaded with dosh, as well as anti-malarial tablets and a hepatitis immunization stuck into my bum.

With love, and I miss you too!
Jim

Later that day, Jim caught the plane, and within two
hours had moved from a wealthy westernized industrial
centre to a poorly developed Third World rice-field/
tourist economy.

12 THE 'I LOVE YOU GIRL' OF BALI

As he was slumbering through a lunchtime hangover, during the two-hour trip to Tuban airport on Bali, a voice whispered into his left ear, 'Hullo, howja doing mate?' The last time he'd heard that voice, asking that question, had been in the early hours of the morning lying exhausted, all energies spent, on the sand at Byron Bay. He kept his eyes closed and waited for more. 'Thanks for your card. I had myself fixed up OK, so you don't have to worry none.' Cindy sounded as if a visit to the local sexual diseases clinic was something she did on a weekly basis. She went on seductively, 'Ya look real cute in that brown skin.' It was the same fit Cindy. He opened his eyes and gazed into her dazzling pale blue discs. 'Christ, I've missed you.' He hadn't meant to say it, he was still furiously angry with her unwelcome gift, but he reached up and pulled her head down and kissed her.

'Hey, enough time for that later, laddy. Now we must start doing our homework.' She pulled away and settled into the seat beside him, tucking long brown legs underneath her as she hoisted a battered edition of *South-East Asia on a Shoestring* out of her drawstring leather satchel. 'I swapped it for a few favours at Darwin. Guy said it

How many children die before their fifth birthday around the world?

Afghanistan 1 in 3
Mozambique 1 in 4
Nigeria 1 in 5
Botswana 1 in 10
Holland 1 in 100

There are 500,000,000 children worldwide who are malnourished. There are 200,000,000 people worldwide who suffer from obesity

Don't imagine all is well in Britain

• in England there are 2,500,000 children who do not get three meals a day
• in 1980, Britain was the eighth poorest nation in Europe
• in 1985, Britain was the second poorest nation in Europe
• while poverty figures in Spain, Belgium, France, Italy, and Greece have fallen, the proportion of children below the poverty line in Britain has increased from one in five in 1980 to one in four in 1985 – and things have got even worse since then

was the bible of these parts. Let's see what he meant. Presume you're heading for Kuta Beach like I am – so let's see what it's got to offer us.' She started to read aloud.

'" . . . we all hit Kuta to start with, so you might as well enjoy it. Basically Kuta Beach is just that, a strip of pretty, pleasant palm-backed beach with some fairly fine surf (and tricky undercurrents that take away a few swimmers every year), plus the most spectacular sunsets you could ask for . . . and particularly spectacular for the crowds of onlookers who are already eight miles high with a little help from some local mushrooms . . . But don't confuse Kuta with Bali . . . if all that Bali means to you is Kuta, and all that Kuta means is Surf City, then to my mind you might as well stay at home." The people writing this stuff seem to know what they like.'

But for Jim, Bali was the promised transition from the westernized values of Australia to those of the Third World – represented by the sea of screaming taxi drivers outside the airport. All it took was 120 minutes. It was as if he had suddenly acquired a more bummish and run-down personality. His hair felt longer, his clothes more bleached, his eyes more pouched and watery, his chin more unshaven, his smile more leery, as the smells, the heat, the dust, the noise – bloody hell, just everything, plus Cindy at his side – hit him. He hitched his bum on to a wall behind the shouting taxi merchants and woefully explained to Cindy how unprepared he felt. He hadn't done any background reading about this culture. He knew nothing about the people, he didn't even know what the local currency was. Travelling was all very exciting, and this was what it was meant to be, but Jim also realized that if he'd bothered to do just a bit of research in advance into what it was going to be like, it would have been infinitely more interesting and rewarding.

'Forget it, mate. Don't even think of moping, we'll

bone up together along the way.' Cindy waved to a passing three-wheeled heap of junk with an engine, and bargained with the Bemo driver for a 400-rupiah ride to Legian Beach, the other side of Kuta, which she said she'd been told was less touristy. 'By another guy, for more favours, no doubt,' muttered Jim under his breath, but he was loving it.

Four hours later, he was a quarter of a mile out to sea, in brilliant white surf, waiting for 'the big one'. When it came, it gently lifted him up on its whispering slope, getting steeper and steeper until he hung for an instant suspended on a wall of white, looking down on a white sandy beach littered with palm trees and dots of tanned bodies, with a flash of mountains in the distance. Then all hell broke loose, and he was smashed down and around, and sucked into the middle of a vortex of solid water trying to smash his brain out. The lighter side was now the up-side, and there was Cindy's form above him, her exquisite slim outline silhouetted against the filtered sky as he burst through at her side. He kissed her and swam out to greet the next one.

With minimal effort, they discovered a 'losmen' to stay in, in a side street off the main beach at Legian. A man sleeping with his wife and five kids in a huge hammock slung across the open space in front of a tiny shack, had agreed to let them have a hut, or as he called it, a 'losmen', for 7,000 rp a night (or as Jim quickly estimated, £2.50). It had been wordlessly assumed by them both that he and Cindy would share the bed. She'd come in with him and dumped her stuff and said, 'Gee, this should do us fine,' and he couldn't think of a single reason for arguing. The place was all he'd dreamt of. A huge bed dipping in the middle from over-use of its springs, clean sheets worn thinner in the middle than at the edges, a window with paint-peeled shutters, a chair and a table, and best of all it was clean, except for a fine sandy dust and a few flattened cockroaches crunched

Cockroaches

Cockroaches enjoy warm, dark, humid places. They're unpleasant to step on in the middle of the night in bare feet as they give a distinct crunch. Their jaws are adapted to chew almost anything. This enables them to engulf bits of animal or plant product. They don't bite humans though. They're into food, paper, clothing, dead insects. (Remember before killing a cockroach, that they eat bed bugs – including the one that might get you. Everything has something to recommend it.) They don't smell too good though, they have a fetid odour. They are also very into survival, and can live for a month without water. On the down side, they can carry hepatitis, cholera, typhoid, salmonella and polio. They are killed by insecticides.

Exercise

Strength, endurance and fitness have come closer to God than cleanliness. People are swimming in pool lanes, cycling along paths, running across beaches, hiking along trails, horse-riding on bridle paths. The streets are alive with the sound of pounding sneakers, the grunts of weight-trainers, and the rock music of aerobics classes.

This is all fine, and physical fitness is certainly a worthy goal, best achieved by something that is both pleasurable and a by-product of our everyday life. Exercise can protect the heart from the early onset of certain diseases, help control our weight, decrease tension, and lower the statistical risk of certain other diseases. It may also raise our spirits and make us feel more alive.

Benefits achieved from different exercises

	Stamina	Suppleness	Strength
Badminton	•	•	•
Canoeing	••	•	••
Cycling	•••	•	••
Disco dancing	••	••	•
Football	••	•	•
Hill walking	••	•	•
Jogging	•••	•	•
Martial arts	•	•••	•••
Rowing	••	•	••
Squash	••	•	•
Swimming	•••	••	••
Tennis	••	•	•
Brisk walking	••	•	•
Weight training	•	••	•••
Aerobics/keep fit	•••	••	••
Rugby	••	•	••
Basketball	••	•	•
Hockey	••	•	•
Netball	••	•	•
Gymnastics	•	•••	•••
Cricket	•	•	

• some beneficial effect
•• very beneficial effect
••• excellent effect

Minutes needed to jog off particular foods:

Food	Minutes
Stick of celery	1.0
Piece of sliced cheese	6.2
Medium apple	6.4
Slice of bread	6.6
Dessertspoon of butter	7.2
Lean chop	11.4
Carton of low fat plain yoghurt	12.4
Carton of fruit yoghurt	20.0
Cheese sandwich	21.6
Cream bun	22.4
Packet of crisps	40.0
Meat pie	50.0
Chocolate bar	52.0

underfoot in the dark. There was no running water, and
the toilet was a shack with a hole in the ground used by
everyone – but who cared? The only nagging reservation
Jim had was that Cindy and he had all the space in the
world, while the family of seven were crammed into a
tiny shack. This raised questions in Jim's mind as to what
backpacking was all about. Was it just picking up stories
and photos to live out on when you got home, without
ever 'touching' a place – whatever 'touching' meant?
He'd have to work that one out later. When he tried
talking to Cindy about his doubts, he was met with a
bland stare and told to, 'Stop moping, matey. Let's plan
out our cycle trip through the mountains for the next
few days.'

Adi, who rented them the hut and supplied them with
tea all day long, knew where they could hire bicycles.
To every query, he replied 'NOPROBLEM' or
'IWANTTOHELPYAMAN' which Jim occasionally
thought meant 'I want to get as much money out of you
as I can, before someone else does'. It was a recurring
worry to him whether the Indonesians were very friendly
because they liked him or just because they needed his
money. When Cindy had asked Adi how much the bikes
would be, he'd first looked blank, then hurt, and finally
puzzled, as if he'd been asked a deep metaphysical question – all the while obviously wondering exactly how
much he could screw them for. But Cindy was a tough
Australian cookie, and the two Third-World, sit-up-and-
beg, one gear, and 'please no worry about the rust, them
is very strong' bikes, hired for a week, finally cost one-
third of the original asking price of 10,000 rp each.

That night, after eating at an open-air restaurant on
the beach, 100 metres from their hut, they'd sampled the
local rice wine with the resulting strange effect of getting
drunk from the feet up, and all in a rush rather than
gradually. One moment Jim was making rational conversation with Cindy, about how far away the furthest

galaxies were (he was struggling with the mathematics of them being 800,000,000 light years away, with the speed of light being 186,000 miles per second and there being 60 x 60 x 24 x 365 seconds in a year – a tricky calculation at the best of times), the next moment he was transformed into a babbling epileptic. But not too epileptic to appreciate Cindy's body as it slipped into bed beside him, bringing with it the most wonderful aphrodisiac in the world: the smell of freshly sun-warmed skin covered in Ambre Solaire with a tiny spice of personal fragrance mixed in. Nor too epileptic to get Cindy to put a condom on him as penance for her past misdeeds and prevention of future ones.

Jim woke up early next morning with instant hungover doubts about the wisdom of having made love again to Cindy. Protection or no protection, it hadn't been a wise decision to make while pissed. However, what was done was done, and the day stretched agreeably out before them. At ten, having left the major part of their worldly goods with a Canadian couple in the next-door losmen, who promised to look after their gear till they got back (in exchange for a couple of bottles of rice wine), they set out on their bicycles for the north coast. Jim, with his sleeping bag wrapped round an exercise book he intended to keep notes in, had only what he stood up in – a white vest top, faded khaki shorts, and his battered pair of trainers. Cindy wore a T-shirt and two prominent nipples, 501s and sandals, and carried a mountain of 'medical' pills – the exact function of which she refused to reveal.

On their creaking bicycles, they headed north across the island towards the mountains, bypassing Denpasar, the capital, but going through towns with names like Sempidi, Lukluk, Mengwi and Marga. They passed stepped paddy fields with little temples by the side of the road between palm trees, going up through village after village into the hills, towards their first goal, Lake Bratan

Bicycles

Cycling is the cheapest, most cost-efficient form of transport (other than walking), and gives you exercise at the same time as allowing you to get to places faster (especially in towns and cities). When petrol runs out, it may be the only sensible form of transport left. However, there are ways of keeping safe while doing it!

Of all cycling accidents, getting knocked out is the commonest, followed by skull and facial injuries. Yet one study of cyclists in an English city showed that only 6% were wearing crash helmets. In a study of regular commuter cyclists, 30% were wearing them, of under 16-year-olds it was 14%, of 16- to 18-year-olds it was less than 1%, and of 18- to 22-year-olds it was again less than 1%.

The advantages of wearing a helmet:

• if all cyclists wore a helmet, there would be a 50% decrease in major injuries
• a helmet makes you much more visible, especially if you wear a white, yellow or red one
• car drivers think you are travelling faster than you are because they associate helmets with motorbikes, and this makes them more wary of you

In Australia it is the law that all schoolchildren have to wear crash helmets on bicycles – why not in the UK?

NO PROBLEM!

in the centre of the island. As they cycled along, they saw a couple of Bemos which had smashed head on into each other. Groups of children from the villages ran alongside them, shouting 'hullo, hullo mister'; and in one village there was a little girl whom Jim would always remember. He had waved at her and shouted 'hullo' as he puffed and wobbled along next to Cindy, and the little girl's face had lit up with a radiant smile that seemed to meet at the back of her head. She'd run towards him shouting 'I love you, I love you', with no understanding of what she was saying – just that smile, big brown eyes and tattered clothes.

On the north side of the island they found whole villages devoted almost entirely to the extraction of tourist money in one way or another. In some places it was only the occasional glimpse of the rice fields, neatly kept and well irrigated, that reminded Jim that not all Balinese life was devoted solely to selling the remnants of their culture to tourists. In one village on the way up, they stopped to look at some wooden carvings some of which, they were told, had taken between four days and four months to carve by hand out of teak and ebony and other local woods. These were sold at stalls by the roadside and the shopkeepers were fighting each other to get at a Japanese group off a bus. As Jim came to a halt, one of the street-sellers noticed him and sprinted over, crying 'Hello, how are you?' with what appeared to be a sincere smile, but at the same time playing with a couple of carvings as if to draw discreet attention to them. 'Where you come from? Oh, English. You want to buy?', and the carvings were put under his nose to be admired. Everywhere Jim went, the guy followed. 'You want?', 'You like?', 'Very cheap stuff.' When Jim ventured, 'But I've no money, I'm just a backpacker,' the response was, 'Ah, we have special backpacker prices.' Jim said, 'But I'm afraid I'm a very poor backpacker,' and back came the reply, 'We have special prices for very poor backpackers.' It was always the same. On the one hand, they had these wonderful friendly receptions from everyone along the way, especially from families and children saying, 'Hullo, how are you, please come in and see us,' and they all seemed genuinely interested, but on the other hand, there was all this obvious intrusive commercialism. Jim wasn't sure what it meant, but it continued to disturb him. If only he had found out more about Balinese culture.

In another village they discovered that an old lady had just died. They were cycling through rice fields when a group of children ran up to them and yelled, 'Come and see this, you've got to come and see this – good festival, good festival.' They followed the children to a clearing where on a huge cremation pyre the body of the old lady was being cremated. It seemed to Jim incredible what was going on – tourists circulating in their sarongs and Hawaiian shirts trying to get better camera angles. Such a complete clash of cultures he found he couldn't watch and turned away. How could something so essentially private be turned into a show? Or was this yet another instance of his lack of understanding of Balinese culture?

Finally, at the foot of the steepest part of the road up the mountain to Lake Bratan, miles from anywhere, with sweat pouring off their exhausted bodies, Jim's front tyre settled slowly and comfortably on to the rim making what had been merely hazardous into something totally impossible. Cursing loudly, Jim got off and shouted to Cindy who was busy proving her Amazonian qualities by slogging along ahead of him into the clouds. Luckily a passing Bemo slammed on its non-existent brakes and managed to stop 150 metres further on. The driver jumped out shouting, his gesticulating arms indicating enormous happiness at the idea of taking them on up to the next village – at a price. However, it proved impossible to find anyone there who had a puncture outfit, and after an uncomfortable night spent on the floor of a sympathetic and welcoming family, Jim managed to per-

suade the head of the household to take him on a moped
to the next village to see if rubber wasn't such a rare
commodity there. Without any means of communication
except gesticulation, and with no bicycle to demonstrate
on (not even a moped as his chauffeur had disappeared),
it was two hours before someone suddenly materialized with a toothy smile and a magic white plastic
box containing all he needed. His luck had changed at
last.

After free-wheeling for the whole of the next day down
the other side of the mountain to Buleleng on the north
coast – a hideously industrialized shanty town, full of
dirt, hassle and noise – they spent the night on the beach,
a couple of miles to the west, and Jim made his first entry
in his 'Bali' diary.

□ □ □

1st March Easy ride all day, swooping down hairpin
bends from Lake Batur. Don't think I've touched my
peddles all day. I'm now sitting watching a magnificent
sunset. To my left is a group of Indonesian women and
children, swimming and washing themselves in the sea.
As the sun disappears, the clouds behind me on the
mountains are lit up from below with an iridescent
orange glow which reflects back in the water. A black
boat with six oars crawls towards the horizon like an
insect on the surface of the silky water. To my right the
beach curves round a line of palm trees, and half a dozen
other fishing craft, their bow lights ablaze, glare
their reflections to us across the water. What a great
day.

□ □ □

One thing about diaries, it passed through Jim's mind,
was that you could, and had to, select what you put in

Sprains

A sprain is damage to ligaments, usually at a joint, when the ligaments and surrounding tissues get torn, twisted or yanked. It frequently occurs at the ankle when your foot turns accidentally and violently inwards (for instance, when trying to play football in rotten shoes on a pitch full of holes).

Most sprains are quite minor but they can be severe and you may even think you've broken a bone. The tear, twist or yank results in pain, tenderness and swelling around the joint, especially when you try and move it.

What to do:

• rest it if possible
• keep the part affected raised as this helps reduce the swelling
• wrap something cold around it, which also helps reduce the swelling and the pain
• put a firm crepe bandage around it to help give it support
• take aspirin or paracetamol for the pain

If it gets worse, or doesn't get better in a couple of days, check with a doctor to make sure there isn't a break. Sprains should improve over forty-eight hours, but it may be several weeks before you can use the joint normally again without any pain.

them. The tendency, though, was to err on the side of
the rose-tinted spectaculars.

□ □ □

3rd March Awful day pushing our bikes back up over
the mountain. No water, long arduous climb, total
exhaustion – not helped by the odd couple of people
with flash bikes and twenty gears who passed us from
time to time. Pushing our bikes was a nightmare. We got
up early in the morning and cycled along the coast, then
we climbed on foot for about six hours on end. Sometimes we had kids walking with us, and we could see the
vegetation really well. It isn't so much tropical as very
green, with palm trees everywhere. I've got some brilliant
pictures looking back down to the sea, with the odd
temple in the foreground.

When we finally got to the top, there was a plateau
and a bit of a cycle ride before we came to these wonderful losmen we had found out about from our book. There
was a game of football going on at the top, although it
was almost night. This Irish guy was playing with a load
of Indonesian kids and he called over saying, 'Come and
join us, fellah, come and join us.' All we could reply was,
'Sorry, we've just pushed these bloody bikes up the hill
for six hours.' We cycled along to the losmen, walked in
and ordered four beers, which we'd been dreaming about
all the way up. The guy running the place said the huts
were all full – we couldn't believe it, not after that day
– but then the Indonesian metaphysical look came into
his eyes. 'There is this one, very nice, cost more money.'
'This' turned out to be a little hut all by itself on the top
of the ridge. It's like a honeymoon hut, which I suppose
it is, but I told Cindy not to get any ideas. We decided
to spend the extra quid or so and it is really worth it.
You have to take opportunities as they come, even if they
occasionally cost a bit more, but everything on the island

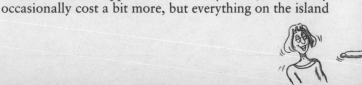

is so cheap, you almost wouldn't notice. The hut even had
its own wood fire, which we lit and warmed ourselves by,
as the nights up here are chilly, then we looked out of
each window in turn at the sunset.

The view is the most amazing I have seen so far. We
had a glimpse of it as we came over the mountain: a
volcano, Lake Batur, and a little village spread out longi-
tudinally along a ridge that forms a line across one edge
of the basin. We are looking over the edge into a big
valley, one side of which is a volcano which erupted
fifteen years ago. Black lava flow with nothing growing
on it is spilling down its side and dominating the valley.
The peak of the volcano casts a long shadow over the
lake, and steep emerald green mountains on the other
side swing right round behind the volcano and appear
on this side forming part of the ridge on which we are
now. Down below us, on the mountainside, are
occasional patches of strip cultivation and rice field, all
surrounded by thick bush. There are other volcanoes in
the distance but their tops are in the cloud all the time.

5th March I'm crashed out here, and this is how it happened – but first I've got to say that you meet some
strange people at losmen. Last night at supper there was
this homosexual American guy with two young homosexual friends. Right in front of them and Cindy, he made
a pass at me. Even with Cindy in tow, I'm beginning to
worry whether I give out the wrong messages.

We spent today whizzing on our bikes downhill,
through village after village, squirting round the bends –
brilliant. We stopped in one village and drank beer and
ate rice and spicy food. I enjoy the food here, though
there's not much meat. They have a great soup, sold by
the side of the road, with noodles and dumplings and
vegetables and lots of spices, so you never know exactly
what you're going to get. Though nothing ever seems to
suit Cindy.

Eventually, we came to this place called Ubud, in the hills north of Denpasar, a very famous town meant to be the artistic capital of Bali where all the hippies go. We were cycling from the market down the main street, called suitably Monkey Forest Road, when we passed a temple full of bad-tempered monkeys throwing things at the tourists. We swerved off to the left, piling down a tiny track to a café which was playing Bob Marley on tape. These sudden detours are one of the advantages of bicycle life. They're very sussed here on Western music, reggae and all the other garbage I like. So we decided to drop in there for a beer. After a day's cycling in the heat, the stuff went straight to our heads.

There was a game of football going on out front, just a group of local Indonesian kids, but I hadn't played since Wales. After the second beer, I tried to get Cindy to come and play, but the Amazonian was too knackered. So I ran out alone, with a sudden incredible amount of energy, and started having a brilliant game. I really went for it, completely forgetting that Indonesian football pitches were not like Wembley. Theirs are rock hard, with bloody great potholes all over the place. I was running down the wing and just went flying into this poor guy, knocking us both over. When I got up I couldn't feel my ankle, it was so painful.

Cindy was in the café with some guy she'd found to talk to. Men are attracted to her like flies, which makes me half really proud to be with her and half crawling with jealousy. When she saw me she burst out laughing. I couldn't walk. An hour later and my ankle had swelled up like a soggy over-ripe melon, and was giving loads more pain. To begin with I just held my ice-cold beer against it, but then Cindy managed to find some ice in the café which they put in a plastic bag.

6th March This is ridiculous. I just can't move. Can't walk, can't cycle, nothing. We're staying on here for

another day. I couldn't sleep last night for the pain. I
took aspirin which helped a bit.

7th March First day back on my bike. I thought I was
being really heroic, but it was probably quite silly. Cindy
gave me a push to get me going and then I wobbled
along, cycling with one foot and just keeping the pedal
turning with the other. I don't have much time in South-
East Asia, and I want to make the most of it. Somehow
I managed to make it back to the beach at Legian, and
am now resting up after collecting all our gear from the
Canadians.

To add to my agonies, Cindy's obviously bored and
keeps disappearing. We seem to have less and less to say
to one another. One bit of compensation was when this
girl came along the beach selling fruit. She was staggeringly beautiful and had a kind of deep throaty laugh. She
was all dressed up for the local festival and gave me this
amazing smile which involved her whole face. I couldn't
understand what it meant. I lay there thinking, 'I'll smile
at him because he's a Westerner with money', or 'I'll
smile at him because he's good-looking and different.' I
didn't know which it was and it threw me. I just didn't
know how to react because I wasn't familiar with the
culture and I couldn't interpret the signals. Maybe there
was yet another reason, even more complicated and less
understandable still?

13 OFF THE BEATEN TRACK IN JAVA

Jim didn't feel together. His ankle and Cindy were both irritating him. His ankle ached, and Cindy was demonstrating the traits he was beginning to dislike most about backpackers: their selfishness, the way they were only really comfortable in the company of other backpackers, and the fact that they didn't seem to see what was around them. What was the point of him travelling around the world to see new things and places and then spending half his time with people he could meet in the pub back home? And again, there was that nagging question at the back of his mind about trying to be 'in touch with' or 'sensitive to' his new experiences. He was aware that they needed to be savoured – the different ways that people 'chose to' or 'had to' live, the whole ecology of their existence. He wanted to understand and yet it all remained stubbornly just beyond his grasp.

He had an argument with Cindy about moving on to Java to get away from the ant-like trail of their fellow travellers. Cindy wanted to stay on Bali but was short of cash. Her parents, whom she happily sponged off,

Smoking

The Joys of Smoking

There must be something about smoking which appeals very strongly to people. In countries such as Indonesia, China, India, and South America over 40% of the adult population smoke. In the UK, 21% of children aged 14 to 17 smoke.

Why people say they smoke

Relaxing
Nice feeling
Makes me hard
Makes me feel sexy
Makes me feel happy
Gives me self-confidence
Makes me forget my troubles
Helps me get on with other people
Other people are doing it so I should too
Makes me feel as if I'm one of the in-crowd

Why people shouldn't smoke

Stinks
Kills other people
Costs a lot of money
Damages unborn babies
Gives you heart disease
Affects children's health
Makes you die before you have to
Kills off your smell and taste buds
It's not nice being addicted to anything
Makes you look stupid and uncaring about
yourself and others
Increases your chances of getting cancer of
the lungs, lips, tongue and cervix

Facts about the world's population:

• there are 5,300 million people in the world
• there are 50 million deaths per year
• there are 120 million births per year
• of these 120 million births per year: 10 million die in
the first year; 10 million die aged 1 to 19; 10 million die
aged 20 to 39

Future health effects on the world's population if present smoking patterns continue:

• There will be 3 million deaths per year from tobacco during the 1990s.
• There will be around 10 million deaths per year from tobacco by 2030.
• About 500 million of the world's population today will eventually be killed by tobacco.
• About 250 million people will still be in middle age when they die from smoking.
• If you have four friends who smoke, on average at least one of them will die from smoking.
• 90% of those killed by smoking will have started smoking in their teens.

So what's the answer?

If you have started smoking – and give up before you're 25 – the chances are that you won't suffer the long-term effects. If you haven't started smoking yet – DON'T. It's bloody hard to give up later because it's so addictive. Lots of people start when they're in their teens, thinking they'll give it up later – but can't and don't.

weren't due to send her more money till Bangkok – and it didn't help that she was already in debt to Jim and angry at her resulting dependency. Jim just didn't appreciate how much it annoyed Cindy, being in his power in this way, but was in turn equally bad-tempered as his gesture towards economy was cutting down on his smoking – even though cigarettes cost practically nothing there. In fact, if he'd bothered to analyse his anger at this point he would have realized that it was as much to do with his continuing dependency on cigarettes as on anything else.

Cindy gave in, she had to, so the next day they caught a cramped bus into Denpasar to search for the National Bus Company terminus. Each bus company ran from a different terminus – three in Denpasar alone Jim noted – and being in a decomposed state, he decided that trying to find anything in South-East Asia was becoming a regular nightmare. It was an aspect of the culture that normally wouldn't have bothered him, but it appeared to be an unpleasant craze of Indonesians to send him off cheerfully in completely the wrong direction rather than admit they didn't know what the hell he was looking for. 'I ask five people the same question and get seven different answers,' he cursed to Cindy.

After an hour and three-quarters of misdirection, they found the right bus station a mere kilometre from where they'd come in. The ticket, including the ferry trip between Bali and Java, and going all the way to Probolinggo in eastern Java, cost them 8,000 rupiah each (the equivalent of about £3 at Jim's estimate), but they got what they'd paid for – a local bus blasting down the roads of Bali, driven by a madman who slammed the brakes on in village after village so that he and his cronies could descend on the local shrine and perform some elaborate ceremony – dropping off a 10 rp note, collecting a flower garland, touching their foreheads with what seemed to be ash – as casually as if they were getting off

Anorexia and bulimia

What are they?

Anorexia means 'loss of appetite'. Anorexia nervosa literally translated means 'a nervous loss of appetite', but is usually taken as meaning 'a chronic loss of appetite and loss of weight caused by a psychological condition'. Bulimia literally means 'a nervous ox hunger', but is usually taken as meaning 'a preoccupation about food with recurrent bouts of over-eating followed by self-induced vomiting, starvation or laxative abuse'.

 Anorexia nervosa and bulimia overlap, and many bulimics have been anorexic in the past.

Anna's story

I eat until my stomach hurts so badly, the only thing I can think of is to throw up to alleviate the pain. This is such an effective method of blocking out any hassles. It's not illegal, it's easy, and at first it's even pleasurable. It seems to work – but only if you kid yourself. When I know I have to throw up, this terrible black hole appears before me and my life is somehow swallowed by it. It gets blacker and blacker. Anything good is forgotten. I get suicidal. There's no way out. I feel imprisoned. I feel I look like a starving child with a horribly distended stomach and ribs. Why do I want to punish myself so much?

I sit on the outside and look in. I can be with a group of friends in the pub. My whole aim will be to persuade someone to buy some chocolate, because I need to start a binge. Why? Boredom? Loneliness? Perhaps I can no longer think of anything else to do. There's nothing to fill the time except food. Other people can talk, write letters, fiddle around, even work. But the severe bulimic knows only food.

Food. Food. FOOD. What can I throw up next? Sometimes when I eat – knowing I'm going to see the food again – I analyse how easy this will be to get up – how much liquid I need to consume to make it easier. Chocolate is delicious but it seems to line the bottom of the stomach like glue – it's really hard and painful to retch it out.

When I go to someone's house, I'm immediately aware of what food people have. If I see a tin, I find myself asking the owner, 'What's in here?' or in a more round-about way, 'That's a nice tin – what's it for?' I feel I'm so pathetic. What sort of a maniac Is intrigued and even spellbound by the contents of a tin?

When I babysit, as soon as the mother has gone out and the child has gone to sleep, I am compelled to explore the fridge and all the cupboards for food. Sometimes when I find myself reading cookery books, I feel like a dirty old man slobbering over porno magazines!

Anorexia

Not surprisingly, anorexia is not found much in the Third World but appears to be a 'Western' invention. It was first described in the seventeenth century, and the incidence has doubled in the last twenty years. It's more common in girls. For each boy with anorexia nervosa, there are twenty girl sufferers. It usually starts in the mid-teens and affects one in 250 16-year-old girls in the UK. Some girls who exercise excessively may also be anorexic. At least 7% of ballet students are anorexic, but not everyone is anorexic who is thin.

What are the signs of anorexia?

• loss of weight (weighing 15% or more below expected normal values)
• an intense fear of becoming fat, even when you are obviously underweight
• a distortion in the way you view the shape and weight of your body. Claiming that one bit of your body is much too fat, in spite of having lost weight
• you refuse to admit there is anything wrong, though you look as though you come from a famine area of the Third World

Bulimia

Bulimics often seem entirely normal, or even erring on the side of being outgoing, strong and giving, but they share with the anorexic the idea that it is odious to be fat. Bulimia, like anorexia nervosa, is much more common in girls than in boys, and overall is much more common than anorexia. It tends to start slightly later than anorexia, and we don't fully understand what it's all about.

What are the signs of bulimia?

• recurrent binges when you might eat fifteen to twenty cakes in an hour
• fear of not being able to stop eating during these binges
• self-induced vomiting

- taking large amounts of laxatives (up to seventy pills a day – though you would be considered distinctly abnormal a long way before that)
- very severe dieting between binges
- obsessive concern with your body weight and shape

Why do anorexia and bulimia happen?

No one knows, but the theories include:

- fear of growing up
- fear of leaving home and becoming independent
- fear of developing sexuality
- it's a depressive illness
- it's related to fashion

A recent study of the nudes shown in the *Playboy* centrefold and the Miss America winners over the last twenty-five years found that their breast measurements and hip measurements have gradually gone down in size (deflationary), while among the US population as a whole these measurements have steadily got bigger (inflationary).

What happens to anorexics in the long run?

One study showed that:

- 40% fully recover
- 30% improve
- 30% have chronic problems (including death for 5% from suicide, malnutrition or sudden unexpected death)

What happens to bulimics in the long run?

Up to 70% continue to have some eating problem, though in the majority of cases this will not severely interfere with their lives. They may also have other psychological problems such as depression, moodiness and generally not feeling good about themselves.

What should you do if you think you are anorexic or bulimic?

Admit you've got a problem and get some help from your doctor, and/or a local self-help group.

for a pee. Though given the way they drove, some kind of protecting god was needed.

They made Gilimanuk just in time for the twenty-minute ferry crossing to the terminus on Java — two kilometres outside Banyuwangi. The boat was christened *Wave Cruiser 9*. What, mused Jim, as yet another iri-descent seascape of light spread from the sunset across the mirror-calm ocean towards him, had happened to the first eight? But he was too exhausted to think about that, and fell asleep immediately on the next stage of the journey, waking six hours later as they came into Probolinggo. He woke Cindy, who'd fallen asleep with her head in his lap, and they staggered out into the thick darkness of 2 a.m. Cindy read out the name of the main street, 'Jalan Raja P. Sudirman', before they collapsed into the Hotel Bromo Permai II and found, even at that hour, the ever-welcoming tea and a room.

To ease their financial worries, they spent the next night in bare simplicity on the floor of a villager's back room in Ngadisari, on the upper slopes of Mount Bromo. And here Jim discovered a new complication. He woke at 3 a.m. to find that Cindy was outside, puking. Rolling over to try and unearth her medical pills, he discovered one box after another of laxatives. Why, he wondered, when every other backpacker was humping around plane loads of anti-diarrhoea pills, was Cindy into laxatives? When she came back in, he questioned her about it and she burst out crying, choking out a sobbing explanation that she had a problem. When she ate too much she had to make herself sick and take laxatives to stop herself getting fat. Jim couldn't believe it. He'd thought she was naturally thin.

A couple of hours later, in dismal mood, they stumbled across the blackened lava sand plain, and up the 246 steps of the inner crater of Mount Bromo to watch the sun come up. It was an all-time downer. The place was packed with other people, it was cloudy, it was drizzling, there was no sunrise, and Cindy was cuttingly sarcastic. She released on Jim all her pent-up feelings of powerlessness, her fury at being taken away from Legian Beach, her fellow backpackers and the kind of life she felt comfortable with, as well as at her recent admission that she might be anorexic. Then suddenly, as they stood there, the clouds cleared and across the steaming valley a huge plume of smoke from another active volcano was visible through the mist, back lit by the sun. Cindy completed her diatribe, saying, '. . . let's dig that one over there, it looks better.' Without a backward glance, she stomped off across the ash plain, her rucksack bouncing on her back.

As it turned out, it was a beautiful day's walk through the lush greenery of the valley, with birds calling to one another from the trees on each side of an endlessly winding path. This was what Jim had craved for when he'd decided to leave Legian Beach: to be off the beaten track, by themselves, walking through this primitive landscape, half-lost, his ankle problems forgotten, his eyes sensitive to everything around – fallen branches, the movement of insects, song birds, and a huge array of colours. He could feel the soft caress of buoyant air against his face, and could smell the hot succulent undergrowth. Every sense was taking on swollen significance, and even Cindy was becoming bearable. Then, as if by some new piece of magic, as the last edges of light were growing dull behind the smoking mountain, they met an old man in rags, weighed down beneath a bundled sheaf of branches, who guided them into a village just as darkness finally swallowed everything.

They were soon sitting on the floor of a tiny, dank room, lit only by the flicker of an open fire, watching the owner of what appeared to be the local eating and drinking house cook them food. While they debated what they would do next, one of the locals came in and crouched down next to them. As he sat back on his haunches, with his shifting eyes, his unsmiling face and his ungiving style, he looked every inch a conman. He had obviously heard they were in the village, and was offering his services as guide for the two-day trip up the smoking volcano they'd been chasing all day. Unwillingly, because they did not trust him but knew he was all they could get, they negotiated a price – bargaining because they'd learnt to bargain about everything. The price settled, he disappeared back into the darkness, with a final, 'Right, you stay here for night, and we get going first thing in morning.'

That night Cindy and Jim slept together in a single sleeping bag for warmth and reassurance, their arms encircling each other, their sweating bodies moving restlessly together. The touch of soft skin was pleasant compared with the discomfort of hard boards underneath. In the cold of yet another 5 a.m. start, they crawled out through near-darkness into the back of a decrepit lorry. Jim was considering crumpling himself back to sleep in his bag, but after a couple of rattling jolts that left bruises across the back of his thighs that were to last for weeks, all they could do was half-crouch in the lorry, hanging on to anything that was even remotely solid, as they were conveyed at a hair-raising pace over a muddy track which wound along ridges half washed away by the rain, with deep ruts and slides down into green jungle each side. After two hours, they were dumped by the edge of a fast-running stream, where they washed before setting out across a long shallow valley, through grass too tall to see over. It was just the three of them, climbing steadily the whole day, meeting no one – their guide skulking on ahead and Jim and Cindy keeping up as best they could, not knowing where they were or what they were doing except that they would get to the top of this volcano or bust.

As on the day before, Jim felt high, all his senses going full blast, glutting himself on exuberance so that it occasionally overflowed into vast leaping shouts of joy at the sheer pleasure of it all. In the afternoon, they overtook a French party, fully equipped with puffer jackets and the latest climbing equipment, who'd obviously spent a fortune on their expedition to this particular volcano. This flooded Jim with an even greater intensity of feeling about their own independent self-sufficiency. It was another step towards him becoming 'a master of the universe', he thought, thankful for the walking he'd done in Wales that was helping him to survive all this activity.

Finally, exhausted, they camped on the edge of a forest at sunset, under a great black explosion of billowing smoke every twenty minutes, lit up from below by the sinking sun. Their plan was to get up again at 1 a.m. and climb to the top of the volcano because, as their guide explained in his faltering English, the final ascent was long and difficult. They would just about manage to reach the top by dawn. As the first semblance of warmth was creeping from their bodies into their sleeping bags, the French party arrived and noisily set up camp nearby, talking and, at intervals, murmuring 'oohs' and 'aahs'.

After a while, Jim's curiosity became too much for him and first he, and then Cindy, crawled out and wandered over to join the others standing on the ridge. A giant electrical storm was flickering back and forth across the sky, lightning illuminating the stack of smoke as it surged out. The clouds lit up again and again, as shafts of white probed backwards and forwards. The gods were playing up here in their element, Jim thought, as he settled back into his bag. His home and his family and friends might as well be inhabiting a different planet from the one he was witnessing.

At one o'clock in the morning they began chomping across loose slippery ash in silent misery, leaden with lack of sleep, each taking their own route as best they could. It was tough, a matter of pure survival, trying not to think of the why's or wherefore's, just stumbling on because it was the only thing to do. There was one point as Jim was climbing up through the clouds when he touched rock bottom. He'd lost contact with the others, he'd forgotten why he was doing this, he wanted out with Cindy, and he was wet, cold, and hungry. Misery washed over him in waves of nausea, as he struggled across the last few metres to join their guide. 'Maybe feeling this awful is just altitude sickness,' his disintegrating mind questioned (unaware that he wasn't even half-way to the 2,500 metre mark where altitude sickness begins to bite). Sparks glowed in the dark as they showered out of the mouth of the crater, making it impossible for Jim to catch more than a searing, red hot glimpse into the molten centre of the earth. He fell asleep clutching in his exhaustion the memory of the most primitive sight he'd ever witnessed.

He was woken by Cindy as the sun was rising over the horizon to see the carpet of clouds below them being lit up pink by the first rays of the sun. At the same time, there was an explosion behind them and the spume itself was lit up pink too. For four hours they stood watching, waiting for each explosion to occur, before skiing back down the ash slopes on their feet and their bums, Jim's bad ankle aching with each twist and bend. To his surprise, now that he was over it, the climb and all it entailed turned out to be the most superlative thing about Java – in fact the best thing about Indonesia as a whole. The best things, he reflected, were undoubtedly those that were hardest to achieve.

Back in Probolinggo, they caught a bus on to Yogya-karta, and then took a becak – a bicycle rickshaw representing the world's most downmarket person-powered taxi – from the bus station to a midtown losmen, a cheap and seedy little prison cell to crash in for a 24-hour wipe-out. It cost all of 1,000 rp (about 40p). Crawling back to consciousness next day, splashing water over each other from a courtyard water tank, they began to recover

Destruction of the rain forests

Every day, more than 150 square miles of tropical rain forest are wiped out or degraded. An area the size of England, Scotland and Wales together was lost last year alone.

Paper

Paper is produced from wood. The amount of paper used in the UK each year involves the destruction of a forest the size of Wales.

Altitude sickness

Symptoms can start at over 2,000 metres above sea level, though the sickness doesn't usually occur until above 3,000 metres. It varies from person to person.

The heights of some places

Mount Everest	8,848 metres
Cuzvco, Peru	3,399 metres
Val d'Isere	1,850 – 3,499 metres
Darjeeling, India	2,265 metres
Mont Blanc	4,807 metres
Mexico City	2,300 metres

their sense of humour and some remote common appreciation of life.

The journey to Borobudur and the eighth wonder of
the world, forty kilometers outside Yogya, was up
through lands resembling a lush sacred garden, with
palms and brightly coloured fruit and flowers, among
which ran broad, winding, glittering rivers. Every kilometre or so into the mountains, they came across bands
of ten or more children, either all boys, or all girls, talking
and messing around together, stopping only to wave at
the passing bus.

Up and up they climbed, until round the last bend they
came upon a crazy-paving temple, tipped this way and
that, covering an entire hill and looking out on to a
mountain that was meant to represent an immense resting
Buddha. The previous year, Jim discovered, an American
company had unsuccessfully tried to buy the Buddha
mountain in order to build an international hotel as a
100-foot high hernia in the Buddha's navel.

On their return to Yogyakarta, Jim and Cindy took a
second-class train on to Jakarta, arriving four hours late,
at 10 a.m. Throughout the night, at each lengthy stop,
hundreds of sellers climbed aboard and walked up and
down the carriages, screaming at the top of their voices
the name of their wares. 'Aqua, aqua, aqua . . . ', they
called again and again, the sound as penetrating as the
high-pitched shrieks of children demanding to be noticed
by neglectful parents. Shattered, they staggered out into
the blaze of Jakarta to be greeted by the usual swarm of
taxi drivers, one of whom seized Cindy's bag and flung
it on to the back seat of his taxi. As she reached in to
recover it, the taxi driver drove off, with Cindy inside
and Jim hanging on to the door. A violent if effective
way of getting custom, thought Jim, clinging on for his
life.

14 UP SUMATRA

The journey from Jakarta on Java up through Sumatra was a nightmare that Jim swore he'd never inflict on even his worst enemy – which was ironic, because his worst enemy at that particular moment happened to be Cindy, who shared the nightmare with him. Life was, he decided, too short and for those three days stood every possible chance of being a great deal shorter. OK, he told himself, so it had been an experience, and if he followed his Java philosophy of 'no joy without pain' it had been an extravaganza – but next time he'd take the boat.

It had started as fun in Jakarta, with their enforced taxi ride. 'A rather informative flow of ethnic experiences,' was Jim's initial reaction but after sixty-two hours, he couldn't have cared a shit for ethnic considerations. He wanted 'out' like 'out' was something he'd never wanted before.

It was the kind of bad dream Jim regularly wanted to wake out of and usually did. He had raging toothache, the seats were too small, and his knees were jammed rigid at chest height against the unyielding wooden back of the seat in front. Most of the Indonesian passengers were vomiting randomly everywhere and the interior of the bus stank of puke. A monkey used them for moun-

Some eary stuff

What level is 'loud'?	Decibels
pop group	120
plane taking off	120
pneumatic drill	100
busy road traffic	80
someone talking	40–58
leaves rustling on trees	10–20
totally deserted snow plain	0

Most personal stereos produce more than 90 dB and some more than 100 dB. Industrial noise safety limits are eight hours at 90 dB or an hour at 99 dB. So beware not to have walkmans at full blast. Sometimes people turn their walkmans up to maximum to drown out other noise – having it at 103 dB on a tube train which is itself producing 90 dB of noise.

If your ears ring, your walkman is definitely too loud and damaging your ears. TURN IT DOWN – or you'll be saying 'eh?' and 'what?' before you're 30, and most people aren't very sympathetic to the deaf, even if they should be.

Note: Cheaper walkmans might be better than very expensive ones as they are not so powerful and therefore won't do so much damage to your ears.

taineering expeditions, clutching their bags, their clothes, their hair, and then farting in their faces.

On top of all this, Jim never failed to be impressed by the death wish of most Indonesian drivers. To begin with, he'd been intrigued to see how this driver handled it – could it possibly be worse than the lunacy they'd endured already? He began to suss at least one reason they drove so fast. It was to terrify themselves into producing enough adrenalin to stay awake. Not so much 'fast', Jim thought, as 'far too fucking fast'. 'Inevitable death' was a phrase that also came frequently to mind.

During the hour and a half on the ferry across the Sunda Strait between Merak on Java and Bakauheni on Sumatra, to soothe his shattered nerves and to annoy Cindy, Jim chatted up an Indonesian student with beautiful high cheek bones and mud brown eyes. She wanted him to write to her when he got home. He took her photograph and promised to send her a copy.

Back on dry land on Sumatra, the road became by turns a single-track gravel path lined with debris, a coconut plantation, a makeshift paddy field, a tidal river, and then back into a single-track path again. The entire journey was one long game of 'Chicken', with confrontation after confrontation between their bus and articulated lorries, other buses, vans, cycles, anything that moved, hurtling towards them at combined speeds of up to 160 kms an hour – all the drivers searching for the psychological weak spot. Jim soon sussed that for the average Indonesian driver, it is a matter of the greatest personal integrity and pride not to give way – even if for the passengers it becomes a cheap, if involuntary, form of suicide. Certainly Jim's driver would not have looked out of place in a straitjacket, with white padded walls as a backdrop. He was on a mission – not to humble Bukittinggi, but to the pearly gates in the upper stratosphere, taking his unwitting and unwilling guests with him.

Farts

In any one fart there are at least five gases – oxygen, nitrogen, hydrogen, methane, and carbon dioxide. Hydrogen, carbon dioxide and methane are made in the intestines by the action of bacteria on food, and some foods are better fart fodder than others. A diet of beans increases the average person's fart factor by ten. Nitrogen, oxygen and carbon dioxide are swallowed into the stomach. Not all the gases in the gut come out as farts. Some come out as burps. None of these gases smell, so what makes the fart stink? Hydrogen sulphide is the chief smell donor, but there are also other chemicals which help the smell stakes – mercaptans and volatile fatty acids.

Everyone farts – so don't believe anyone who says they don't. Normal people fart 300 to 2,000 cubic centimetres a day, with an average of 500 cc. As suggested above, it's best to stand well clear of vegetarians, especially if their only diet is beans! The average number of farts per day is 13.4, and the record number of farts in a day is said to stand at 34. This should, with a little effort and many cans of beans, be easy to beat. *The Guinness Book of Records* is waiting.

Toothache

Toothache most commonly occurs when the nerve endings in the teeth become exposed, either through wear and tear, or because a filling has fallen out. These nerve endings are very sensitive and when they come into contact with something hot or cold, or pressure is put on them, they give pain. The 'feelings' of the nerve endings can be temporarily deadened by using the oil extracted from cloves (chewing on cloves themselves helps too). There is also something new on the market – a bit like Blue Tack – which can be used where a filling has been lost or is needed (a DIY dentist's kit).

A less common cause of toothache is infection in or around the root of a tooth. If left, this can form an abscess – a collection of pus made up of dead white cells from your bloodstream which collect together to try and cope with the bacteria. The pressure of the swelling and pus associated with the infection causes the pain. If the abscess bursts the pain disappears. This pain can also be helped by using the oil extract of cloves. However, the best treatment for tooth infections is antibiotics (hopefully in your first-aid kit – see Chapter 3) to kill off the bacteria. If that does not work – see your dentist as soon as you get back, as things may not always clear up completely.

Travel sickness (motion sickness)

Charles Darwin, Lawrence of Arabia, Nelson and Caesar all found that travel made them sick, but it didn't seem to stop them travelling.

Why do you get it?

No one quite understands why travel sickness happens, but it seems to involve the inner part of your ears – the 'vestibular mechanism', a series of very small interconnected semicircular tubes – some horizontal and some vertical – which contain a tiny 'stone'. The position of the stone in the semicircular canals tells you which way up you are relative to gravity and what your eyes see.

What do you feel?

The first sign of travel sickness is feeling less active and not wanting to talk. This is followed by nausea, an increased production of saliva, a feeling of light-headedness, increasing apathy and depression, and a 'cold' sweat. These symptoms can get so bad you can actually start to wish that the boat you are sailing in will sink, the plane you are flying in will crash, or the car you are travelling in will smash. Why some people get it and other people don't no one knows.

What to do?

We all have to travel at some time, so if you can:

• experiment with various travel sickness tablets; different ones suit different people
• try 'stick on' patches from which the medicine is absorbed through the skin and 'pressure point' bands which work like acupuncture exerting pressure at specific points on your wrists
• on boats, try staying on deck in the fresh air which will delay the onset of sickness. When it starts, try lying face downwards pointing along the length of the boat
• in cars, keep your eyes on the horizon. It is interesting that most drivers don't get sick, only the passengers
• don't read in cars, even for short periods of time

You're not a weakling if you get sick – it happens totally at random. Some people are travel sick when young and then it clears up. Other people get travel sick when they start something new – like sailing – but then with experience it goes away.

The human faeces mountain and the human faeces sea

There are 5,300,000,000 people in the world. An average human turd weighs around 250 gms (OK, so yours is a bit more, but who's counting?). That makes one and a quarter billion kilos of shit per day on a normal day. On a bad day we'd be able to fill the whole of the Mediterranean, and some might even flow over into the Atlantic. (If you swim in the Mediterranean, you'll probably be able to confirm these facts.)

Pee production

Our kidneys receive about 1,872 litres of blood every twenty-four hours. From this blood, the kidneys filter out 200 litres of fluid, but almost all this gets reabsorbed while still in the kidneys, and on average we produce only about 1.5 litres of pee per day. If you drink more, you pee more, and if you drink less, you pee less – clever, the human body. Sometimes when you drink very little, your pee is very concentrated and smelly. This doesn't mean that anything is wrong.

There were, however, some exquisite moments of rare
semi-relief when the bus stopped. Where — Jim couldn't
have cared less. He staggered out at one place, and was
walking around to relieve the cramp in his legs when a
figure materialized out of the forest with a bees nest and
gave him a great chunk of honeycomb. He gave some to
Cindy and they stood there, oblivious to their surroundings, chewing away on this marvellous unexpected feast,
with honey dripping down their faces on to their clothes.

At another stop, he'd got off in a town, desperate to
find a public toilet. As he walked in, there was a gnarled
thug at the entrance collecting money, but Jim, with
another pressure to relieve, ignored him — only to discover to his horror that the 'toilet' was a hole in a piece
of concrete with a generous layer of surrounding shit.
The smell, the flies, and the mess were indescribable. It
was all he could do not to gag as he tried to hit the hole
from a distance. (He felt he could have done with a laser
guidance system like that used by the Americans in Iraq.)
Even so, on the way out, the guy held out his hand
saying, '50 rupiah for using.' Jim could not believe it. He
walked straight up to the table, scraped the shit off his
shoes against the table legs, shouted 'Fuck off' and stal-
ked out.

After three days and three nights of constant travel,
with two mechanical failures and as many mental ones,
they arrived at Padang, where the driver informed them
that to get to Bukittinggi they needed to change on to a
local bus. It was 4 a.m., and in the last sixty-two hours
they'd had maybe three hours sleep, all on the road. The
next bus to Bukittinggi was at 6.30, and the only place
to wait was a small bus depot, already crammed with
twenty or more Indonesians crashed out on the floor.
Then on arrival in Bukittinggi they discovered that the
bus station was three kilometres out of town and they
had to walk. Cindy by now was in tears and refusing to
speak, not that Jim could have cared less.

The greenhouse effect

What is it?

The greenhouse effect occurs when the heat of sun rays reaching earth is trapped in our atmosphere by certain gases which act like a kind of one-way permeable blanket. Without these atmospheric gases, the sun rays would radiate back into space. The natural greenhouse gases include carbon dioxide, methane, nitrous oxide and water vapour. They all exist in small amounts in our atmosphere. The trouble starts when they begin being produced in vast amounts by something we humans have devised.

Carbon dioxide comes from:

• burning forests (which has a double effect, as the burning produces carbon dioxide, and the destruction of the trees means that there is less green vegetation to absorb the carbon dioxide)
• burning coal and oil in power stations
• cars
• cement production

Methane comes from:

• vegetation rotting under water (rice fields)
• waste gases (farts) from cows, humans, sheep and termites

Nitrates come from:

• the breakdown of fertilizers

Then there are the problems of 'man-made' gases like chlorofluorocarbons (CFCs) which are now being banned, but were being used in aerosols, foam plastic, refrigerators and air conditioners (and still are in some countries). Some CFC molecules are 10,000 times more powerful than carbon dioxide in their greenhouse effect.

CFCs also damage the ozone layer which helps to filter the ultra-violet (UV) light from the sun rays on their way in. This UV light screening is important because it's this element of sunlight which is one of the causes of skin cancer.

What are the results of the greenhouse effect?

The greenhouse effect has led to the prediction of increasing temperatures on the earth as a whole by about 1.3 degrees Centigrade by 2030 and 3 degrees by 2070. This would bring about greater climatic changes than have occurred over the last 10,000 years, and could result in sea levels everywhere rising by a metre or more. For every one metre rise in the sea level, all shorelines around the world would shrink up to 300 metres. The effects of this would hit developing countries hardest – the Nile delta in Egypt, the Ganges delta in India, the coral atolls, and the whole of the Indian ocean would be particularly vulnerable, with 200 million people or more losing their homes.

Can we do anything about it?

The answer is 'Yes.'

Transport:

• fewer, rather than more, cars by increasing public transport, using bicycles, and so on.
• catalytic convertors on all motor vehicles to cut down on exhaust fumes.

Rain forests:

• stopping further destruction of rain forests by developed countries providing more aid to developing countries. Having enjoyed the fruits of destroying our own forests, we should not expect other countries to do without the financial benefits brought about by exploiting natural resources.

Industry:

• providing economic aid to the Third World, including tree planting programmes and help with the production of environment friendly cars and fridges.
• developing environment friendly forms of energy production from renewable resources like the wind, waves, and sunlight. The cost of producing a therm of heat by solar power has already come down from $56 to $14. It needs to come down to 25 cents per therm to make it economically viable.
• increasing energy preservation by better insulation methods.

Rich nations have 25% of the world's population and use 70% of the world's energy.

After two collapsed days at the Gango Hotel, Cindy had recovered enough to let Jim hire a local motor bike and pelt up to the equator. This was represented by an ulcerated concrete globe by the roadside, in a paddy field in the middle of nowhere. They stopped and did handstands, somersaults, bunny-flips, backwards and forwards across the imaginary magical line, so that later on they would be able to say, 'Oh, the equator – yeah, crossed it loads of times.'

Next morning, sitting together on the back seat of yet another bus, on the way up to Samosir Island on Lake Toba, Cindy – looking, Jim thought, tired, thin and scraggy – started reading out of the *Shoestring* guide. 'The island is a centre for the likeable Batak people and you can see plenty of their high-peaked Batak houses in Tomok, the main village. Greet people with a hearty "Horas!" (It didn't say why, or what would happen to you as a result.) The island is very beautiful, very simple, and the deep green lake invites swimming.'

Only half-listening to this, Jim realized that for half an hour the bus had been stuck behind two trucks travelling at 20 kms an hour and refusing to move over. As they finally pulled into a passing place, the bus drew level and stopped, with the drivers shouting into one another's faces. One of the truckies then descended slowly and took a swing at the bus driver through his open window. At which the bus driver immediately gobbed in his face, let in the clutch and shot off. Out of the back window, Jim, sitting hypnotized by this scene of violence, saw the trucky reach into his cab and draw out a half-metre long machete, run after the bus, and launch it at them like a professional knife-thrower. Mouth open, mind in neutral, Jim watched the spinning missile cover the distance and embed itself in the steel panel of the bus, a couple of centimetres below his window.

Soon they only had two days left in Sumatra. Their flight out of Medan was fixed and they had to make it, so they decided to travel on to Bukit Lawang, 80 kms north-west of Medan and deep in the rain forest. There they booked into a losmen along with a couple of guys they had originally met in Byron Bay, and spent a peaceful evening eating, drinking and swapping travel stories. They had arranged for a local guide to take them to an orang-utan reserve in the rain forest the following day, but after the previous night's food binge Cindy puked all night, and at dawn rolled over and refused to move.

Jim spent a pleasant day wandering through the forest with some other tourists and a couple of guides, listening to the monkeys and looking at the orang-utans. He'd hear a big crash, and there they'd be, the kings of the forest not caring a toss about him. If they wanted to get somewhere, they just went direct, no mucking around — even if it meant knocking down a few trees along the way. Jim was really into it, and completely lost sight of the fact that he and Cindy had to catch the last bus out to Medan at 5 p.m. for their flight the next morning. He'd explained all this to the guide, who'd said, 'Yeah, yeah, no worries, no worries. I'll do that.' At 4.30 p.m., Jim made what he hoped was a cool-sounding remark about getting back. The guide looked at him, at his mate, at his watch, and said, 'Ah yes, we have problem. We go, the rest walk with other guide.' They took off at a brisk trot, soon started running, then suddenly they were pelting through the forest in a fair imitation of an orang-utan, swinging on the vines and jumping over the vast tree trunks. Jim powered on, sweat pouring off him in the humidity, desperately trying to keep up with his guide as it became a racing certainty that he was going to miss the bus. Not a too brilliant way to end the day.

Finally, they broke out of the forest covered in mud, sweat, and flies, carving a way through a crowd of startled tourists who had come to watch wildlife and were suddenly faced with these two madmen. They cleared the space across to the river canoe ferry, shouting

Food, flies, fingers and faeces

These four 'F's are ways in which diseases causing diarrhoea, vomiting and other horrors spread. Remember flies are equally happy feeding on faeces as on food.

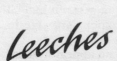

Leeches

Leeches live on land and in water. They love humans – and any other warm-blooded animals that might be passing. They attach themselves especially to the lower part of your legs and your ankles. Trousers and socks are no protection and they can even get down your boots. Once they're attached, they suck your blood, swell up, and are difficult to remove until they decide they've had enough. If you pull them off, bits of their mouth parts sometimes get left behind. The best treatment is to put salt, alcohol or vinegar on them, or if these are not handy, use a lighted match or a cigarette.

and yelling at the guy on the other side. He must have thought that someone was dying, the way he hauled the boat across to them with total disregard for the waiting passengers. Reaching the other side, they started running up the bank just as the bus was leaving.

Jim screamed and waved at it, and the driver shouted back that he would wait. Jim grabbed his bags (Cindy was already aboard with hers), begged two more minutes, took off all his clothes, and plunged into the river. It was cool and beautiful. Getting out, he shook hands with his startled guide, thanked him, and tipped him 1,000 rp. He climbed panting into the bus beside a furious Cindy, who'd been convinced that he was going to miss it. As he sat down, he squashed something on his thigh, and pulling up his shorts he found three fat leeches sucking away next to his balls. Cindy screamed as Jim hopped up and down, yelling and pulling at the bloody parasites, watched by an audience of astonished locals.

It had been an incredible day. His last memory of Indonesia was of a girl at the side of the road, with a baby on one hip and a huge basket of washing on top of her head. She looked at him with an expression of complete calm, and he longed desperately to say something to her, to put into words how wonderful it had all been. But he had no words, no common language to express it all in.

Medan, the capital of Sumatra, had no appeal whatsoever except for its international airport. It was a relief to escape from the dirty rubber plants, the stinking motor bikes and the polluted streets of the city. Though even the airport runway was littered with battered, burnt-out Dakota corpses as they took off for the twenty-minute flight to Penang. Their intended journey by ferry had been cancelled, as the boat had sunk the week before in a storm. Maybe that was the reason for the Wave Cruiser between Bali and Java being number 9.

15 THAILAND, CINDY DEPARTS, A FRENCH LETTER ARRIVES

Things remained tense between Jim and Cindy during the journey by boat from Penang across to mainland Malaysia, and on up by bus to Sadao at the Thailand border. After another seventeen hours, they eventually reached Bangkok, where Cindy, who was off to India, finally paid him the money she owed. This diversion prevented Jim from being able to stop off in South-East Thailand on the way to Bangkok, causing his relationship with Cindy to deteriorate even further.

But when the moment of parting finally came, Jim was filled with a confused mixture of feelings. They had, after all, shared not only the same bed but many other experiences too. Unfortunately, the things which used to attract him to her – her physical beauty, her positive attitude to life, her unpunctuality, the way men were always trying to pick her up – now irritated him. He was no longer even sexually attracted, her scraggy anorexia repelled him, and she was certainly no soul mate.

Sitting in the Southern bus station, clutching in one hand a 225 baht (£5) bus ticket to Surat Thani, and in the other a letter collected from Bangkok main post office (off Tanee Road), Jim had an unusual spasm of insight.

Ladies and lagers

Some lagers now popular with women have a high alcohol content. However take note, women are more sensitive to alcohol than men. This may be because on average women weigh 15% less than men, and a smaller percentage of their total body weight is made up of water (50% rather than 60%). There is therefore less to dilute the alcohol, and women get higher blood alcohol levels for the same amount of drink.

Women also absorb more or less alcohol depending on the time of their menstrual cycle, the highest absorptions occurring around or just before their period. Women on the pill get rid of alcohol more slowly.

And it's not only men who have sexual problems with alcohol. Studies show women do too. Women who drink heavily don't enjoy sex so much. They are less interested, and it tends to be more painful. Low alcohol beer may be a better option!

How fast do you get drunk?

Certain drinks pass into the bloodstream faster than others, depending largely on the strength of the drink. Fortified wines, like sherry, are quickest – one reason why alchies tend to drink sherry (that and its cheapness). Spirits, like whisky and gin, if taken neat cause the stomach to produce a protective lining of mucus which stops them being absorbed so rapidly. The exit to the stomach goes into spasm or shock and the alcohol can't get through to the first part of the intestine where it gets absorbed. However, it is going to get through in the end, so you may be lulled into a false sense of not being as drunk as you're about to get.

Turning things over in his mind, he began to perceive that sexual attraction between people might be a funny mixture of a whole number of different things – looks, smell, style, energy, sense of humour, shared views, and many other things besides – some of which worked and some of which didn't. Cindy and he had had to make various compromises to keep their relationship going, but there had come a point when these compromises were no longer worthwhile. It was then that everything had fallen apart.

At the same moment, Jim also saw that he was not exactly a knight in shining armour himself. He was quirky, moody, didn't like the endless company of other backpackers, and probably fell far short in understanding Cindy's needs, but before his ego took the mangling it deserved (Jim's insights rarely survived infancy if they involved his ego), he noticed that the letter he'd picked up was from Jane. He tore it open.

□ □ □

18 Rue Monsieur Le Prince, Paris
(Started in September but finished in February)

Dear Jim – Greece was great, but the real excitement happened here. You remember me telling you in Wales that we were going grape-picking in Languedoc? Well, Kate and I finally got to France by a series of trains and hitches, and met up with David and John. John was in the year ahead of us. Did you know him? He joined the army and has six weeks leave before going back to the desert. They drove down together in David's yellow 2CV (yeah, the same one – you wouldn't have thought it could do another kilometre, would you?), crossed over on the Dover to Calais night ferry, and arrived in France at 3 a.m. After a bit of hassle trying to explain to the French gendarmes that the bits of string were holding the roof load on, and not the car together, they finally joined us for supper just as all the other grape-pickers rolled up. We're all staying in a very basic outhouse provided by one of the farmers, with strict instructions about looking after the place. Some hope – with so many bodies around, it's not been easy. The lav stinks of pee. Why can't your sex aim straight?

All in all, the meeting-up was a smoothly run operation – since when things haven't been too ace. Everyone's job started next day, apart from mine, which meant basically that I got up to a filthy, breakfast-strewn kitchen. I'd just managed to clear up and get lunch on the table before the workers, including Kate, traipsed in – full of grumbles, aches and pains – wolfed down their food and left, leaving a trail of washing-up in their wake. Then, being the only one available, I had to drive David's 2CV to Montpellier to pick up the remainder of the party – Gary, John's friend from the army, and his girlfriend Daisy.

I got lost in Montpellier, and finally arrived at the station, hot and flustered and forty minutes late, to find Gary and Daisy having *café au lait* outside in the sun. All right for some! On the way back a woman in front of me screeched to a halt. I just stopped in time and was congratulating myself on my fast reactions when there was a huge crunch as six cars piled up behind me and sent me forward into the car in front. That was the final straw. I got out of the car preparing to have a total breakdown when I noticed that Gary had blood spurting out of the back of his head.

So there we were at the side of the road, being pathetic crash victims, with me holding a hanky firmly over Gary's spurting head and Daisy having hysterics. There was great drama as a woman with a whip-lash was strapped to a stretcher, and when the police arrived we were all breathalysed. A glamorous chic nurse, dressed in whiter than white and looking straight out of a hospital soap opera, grabbed Gary, gabbled some French into his face, and packaged him into the ambulance. Luckily he had his E111 with him, but Daisy had forgotten hers, which was stupid as she still had the risk of being driven home by me.

In the end, it took a very pathetic tearful female act from me to persuade the police to take us to collect our car from the garage where it had been towed. We had to pay the garage 350 francs (about £35), in spite of the fact that they hadn't done anything except take it away. I just hope David's insurance will cover this and the damage. Luckily David seems almost to appreciate yet another dent to join all the others. He says it adds to the style. I'm now quite recovered and am sitting in bed writing this while everyone else, including Gary and his three stitches, is at a local café getting wrecked.

It's been a week since I wrote all that. For some reason, this letter has been lying lost amidst the vendage squalor. I've started working and it's back-breaking. We begin at 7.30 in the morning, and that's not easy because we always wake up hungover from the night before with only five minutes to get to work. The coffee and the gas run out simultaneously as if they are in league against us. The loo is clogged up with eight other people with one purpose, and you end up running to work, unfed, half-dressed and desperate for a shit.

This letter is to give you a true impression of what it's like working in the vineyards – which is not as glamorous as it sounds. It has given me a totally different opinion of wine, let me tell you – the stuff is literally sweat and blood (mine) – but our free allowance is going down well. A good day's work makes you feel you deserve all the self-indulgence you can get, and so every evening is spent wallowing in alcohol and good French food. (Well, that is if you count 'boil in the bag' frankfurters and French bread as French food. They're really good anyhow.)

Rape

What is rape?

Rape is the crime of forcing a female to submit to sexual intercourse. Most women would say it is 'being made to do it when you don't want to'. In the UK, it is now accepted that if a husband 'makes his wife do it when she doesn't want to', this can be considered as rape.

Myth: Rape only happens to young, attractive women.
Fact: Rape happens to children and to women in their eighties.

Myth: Rape only happens if you 'ask for it' by being fresh or dressing in a sexy way.
Fact: Women who are not fresh and sexy also get raped. Being fresh and sexy does not mean you want to get raped.

Myth: Most rapes are inter-racial (black men raping white women).
Fact: Most rapes are by a man of the same race as the woman (in the USA, this is true for 90% of rapes).

Myth: Rape is committed by strangers out of the blue.
Fact: About 50% of rapes are committed by someone the victim knows, and probably most rapes are carefully planned.

Myth: Some women want to be raped and even dream about it.
Fact: Some women may like physical aggressiveness in sex, but rape is more than this and involves unwanted violence.

How to avoid being raped by strangers

(1) Walk in the best lit part of the street – avoid the shadows.
(2) Walk confidently.
(3) Pretend you're not frightened even if you are.
(4) Avoid eye-contact.

(5) Don't hitch-hike alone if you're a girl.
(6) Don't go home alone with any strange men.

Rape statistics

Offences of forcible rape:

USA (1988)	92,500
New York State (1988)	31,000
UK (1987)	3,200

You bum! I haven't heard a word from you, so I never sent this letter. I'm now 'au pairing' for a couple of French slave-drivers – cleaning all day and babysitting for a screaming idiot all night. This next bit's depressing. I have to tell you about a really awful thing that happened, and has virtually ruined Paris for me. Everyone knows about rape, but for most people it's one of those things that they see in the movies, or read about in the paper – like winning the lottery or, more to the point, like losing at Russian roulette. It's something that happens to other people, on dark streets late at night, and to girls wearing short skirts and walking alone. And I don't do any of that, as you know.

I'd been invited to a friend's house on the Rue St Germain. When I got there, he wasn't in (perhaps I'd got the day wrong, I never did find out). His flat mate was there, and he asked if I wanted something to drink. I said I'd like a coffee (playing safe – I didn't know the guy), and when I'd drunk it I decided I'd leave. However, he decided I wouldn't, and his argument was stronger. He locked the door and removed the keys and I was there until 6 a.m.

My first reaction was sheer disbelief, and the feeling that this couldn't happen to me. To begin with I thought I'd be able to talk him out of it – how naive can you be? Then when I realized talking was fruitless and physical resistance was too, total panic took over. Women *aren't* as strong as men. At one point I was sure I was going to die. Later that seemed like something to hope for. In the end, I just felt resignation, and a determination to endure, and survive.

I had to keep my mind under control, so I thought about my family at home in England, the French class I'd been to earlier that day, the work I still had to do. But my mind kept returning to that room and to what was happening to my body. I thought of all the pets I

Depression

Everyone feels angry and fed up from time to time, in fact a study carried out on 14- to 17-year-olds found that 8% felt fed up or depressed every day, 28% at least once a week, and only 3% of girls and 7% of boys never felt depressed. However there does appear to be a difference between feeling generally fed up and really depressed.

Some of the things that happen to you when you are really depressed:

• you stop enjoying anything
• everything seems a burden
• you feel tired all the time
• you never see the good side of anything, only the bad
• you begin to feel guilty about a whole lot of things that happened in the past
• you may feel irritable and anxious over a long period of time
• you may have suicidal thoughts and feel that life is not worth living
• you may start waking really early in the morning even though you are tired
• you feel worse in the morning and better in the evening

- you go off your food and may lose weight
- your sexual drive decreases
- women sometimes stop having periods

Why do you get depressed?

(1) Some people are more sensitive to getting depressed than others, and certain types of depression do run in families. In such cases, the chemicals in the brain seem to play a part.

(2) Sometimes there is good reason to be depressed: the death of someone you love; losing your job; failing all your exams.

(3) Sometimes there appears to be no good reason – it just happens.

(4) Mostly it's a combination of all these factors together.

What helps depression?

The important thing to remember, though it may be difficult to convince yourself at the time, is that most depressions get better. Remember also that it is not your 'fault' that you're depressed. Depression is an illness and needs to be treated like any other illness. Describing your feelings and discussing them with friends and family may help. If not, then the next thing to do is to talk to an 'expert' like a counsellor or doctor (family doctor, psychotherapist or psychiatrist). Sometimes your body helps itself, or you may have to take anti-depressant medicines. It all takes time. But don't be ashamed to ask for help, because help can HELP.

Suicide

It is not unusual to have suicidal thoughts at one time or another. Unfortunately, in the UK:

- About 5,000 teenagers a year try to commit suicide, though most of them do not actually want to kill themselves; rather they want to draw attention to how they are feeling.

• There are 120 successful teenage suicides a year, and in two out of three cases there seems to be a definite reason.

If you know someone who is feeling suicidal, you should take it seriously and try and encourage him/her to get some help. The main feelings that occur before someone attempts suicide are loneliness, hopelessness, rejection, anger, and worries about the future.

The main reasons given by teenagers who have tried to commit suicide are school work they can't cope with, arguments with parents, family break-up, worries about getting a job, and boy/girlfriend problems.

had ever owned, naming each of my cats in turn: Oscar, Mittens, Lionel . . . what was the name of the fourth one? Herman? Oliver . . . ? Then my mind came back to the room. I tried to think of ways to get out. I told him it was morning and I'd be missed. He took no notice. I said I had to use the lavatory. He wouldn't let me go alone. And these interruptions made him angry, and made his actions worse.

Finally he let me go. He didn't seem at all afraid of what I might do, and when the police went to arrest him that afternoon, he'd made no effort to hide the evidence. Yes, I did report it. I reported it immediately. I didn't shower, or change my clothes, although I desperately wanted to. I went to a centre for students that's open all night, and told them what had happened. They called the police, and I spent the entire day reliving the whole experience with three French women police officers.

The bloke was arrested, but he wasn't convicted. His defence lawyer said I'd asked for it. There was plenty of evidence of rape, but it's incredibly difficult to get a successful rape conviction, especially if you are a foreigner in another country.

I feel I'll never really get over it. It's become part of my emotional landscape, something I hold in the back of my mind and don't want to talk about. I keep wondering what I could have done differently, and I keep blaming myself for being so stupid. For a time, I kept having baths three or four times a day, and I have recurring nightmares. It's uncomfortable being around friends, but impossible being alone. I've stuck it out here to try and get my confidence back. My parents came out for a while, and they were terrific.

I don't know why I'm loading all this on you. I just thought you might understand. I feel I'm losing contact with all my friends, so I'm finally posting this letter. It's out of date, but you're not out of mind.

   With love — Jane

□ □ □

'What a fucking bastard,' Jim reflected. 'And I thought I'd got problems.' He sat for a while, thinking about her letter, and watching the nightmare activity of the bus station — in fact, not so much a nightmare as a living hell, with all its errant inmates trying to escape at once. The place was packed with fuming buses, but no one was able to find the one they wanted, including most of the drivers. There were twenty different bus companies, all with identical buses of the same make and colour and with the same number. Someone would call out, 'Here it is,' and point to a bus, and the whole crowd would surge forward praying it was theirs. Then there was a mad scramble to get aboard, with those on first then trying to get off, as they discovered it wasn't actually the one they wanted after all. Jim was directed to six different places before he finally found a bus that was going to Hat Yai, but would drop him off along the way at the port of Surat Thani on the east coast, where he could get the hydrofoil to the island of Koh Phangan.

16 BONGED UP IN KOH PHANGAN

At the port of Thong Sala on Koh Phangan, Jim walked through the hoards of taxi drivers and sat for a few minutes on the edge of a wall, sorting out what he wanted to do. This was a trick he'd learnt from experience. Since Bali, whenever he arrived at a new place, there was this hassle of crowds of people wanting you to do this, live here, go there. The only way he could handle it was to detach himself for a bit, say, 'No, thank you, I don't want anything,' and then walk away and work out exactly what it was that he did want: find a losmen, look for a post office, take a Bemo to a certain place. Whatever it was, you had to work it out in advance, and roughly how much you wanted to pay.

When he was ready, he walked over to a man standing calmly apart from the others at the side of the pier, a broad Cheshire cat grin across his face and a vacant gaze in his eyes. 'Yessir, can I help you, sir? My name is Panchai.' 'Taxi?' Jim queried, suggesting a price. 'Yessir, no problem. One deluxe taxi coming up, sir,' and he pointed to a 1960s motorcycle. 'Takes three people, sometimes four. Now we take my Kong back too.' Panchai's 'Kong' turned out to be his Muslim helper, weighing in at about 130 kilos.

After three attempts, Panchai eventually got the motor-cycle engine to fire, and Jim was placed with his bum sticking four inches out over the precipice of the motor-cycle's pannier, with Kong sandwiched between them like a vast hamburger in an undersized bun. Panchai swerved the bike backwards and forwards across the dust track representing the island's main arterial road, shouting non-stop above the clapped-out motorcycle engine. Half-way down the road they slowed to a pathetic plopping halt, as the engine gave up hope and died.

'Oh,' said Panchai, 'never happened before. But no problem, we walk a little way – very good for becoming fit.' Jim was doubtful whether he needed this, but they took it in turns to wheel the infernal machine to what was flatteringly called a 'filling station' – a rattan mat shack containing a 225-litre drum of petrol on a table, with a plastic tube running out of it. Gravity feeding the petrol into the motorcycle's tank, they discovered it was running equally fast out of a rust hole. 'No problem,' said Panchai, fishing some putty out of his pocket and stuffing it into the hole, 'but we need to take another taxi while it dries.' He stuck his hand out for a lift in a passing pick-up to Panchai's Camp, a few kilometres down the road.

Jim's ramshackle hut on the beach was ideal, and later that evening Panchai's head appeared silhouetted against the open door, interrupting Jim's view of white sand, sea and, in the distance, Koa Samui. Panchai was inviting Jim to eat with him next door, at the Free Love Café, where even the breakfast menu read, 'toast and honey 5 baht, muesli 4 baht, and one bong free'. With a sigh of relief at the sight of Western food again, Jim had a fabulous meal of porridge, banana pancakes, bacon sand-wiches and fruit – guavas, mangoes and lychees – all washed down with 'La Cow' (a cheap form of jet fuel).

Jim didn't miss Cindy at all. He'd found the experience exhausting. Even so, of all the memorable scenes on Koh

Phangan, the one that remained in his mind most clearly had featured a beautiful naked woman. He was swimming in the sea the next morning, in crystal clear water above white sand. Ducking down, he swam a few yards under water, and came up to find her standing there on the edge of the beach – long blonde hair, brown skin, and a black 'v' of pubic hair. White beach, blue sea, palm trees, desirable naked lady – what more could he ask?

That afternoon, Jim went with Panchai back to the port at Thong Sala to help him try and entice a couple of nubile tourist beauties for themselves. The selection that afternoon was poor, and Panchai's attempts to collect someone pathetic. While other taxi drivers and bungalow owners fought one another like maniacs to get the attention of potential customers, Panchai sat on the wall of the pier, smiling vacantly and directing people to other parts of the island from his own. However one stray, Sally – a slightly strange and wacky secretary from London – persuaded Panchai to take her aboard.

Jim considered the Free Love Café, where they took her, to be one big bureaucratic fuck-up. It was run by about fifteen people, half of whom were in a semi-coma. Occasionally someone would come to Jim's table and take an order, but before they could make their way back to the kitchen, they'd crash out on the sofa at the half-way stage. The only people who had any idea how to run the place were a couple called Myum and Kasse. Myum was Thai, and gave people massages and tattoos while they ate. Kasse was a vague but kind English girl from the Channel Islands, who'd come out nine months before and decided to marry Myum and help run Free Love. They had a small adopted son, whose favourite pastime was playing darts. He'd stand at the entrance of the café and hurl darts over the heads of the stoned guests at a board mounted in the kitchen. During Jim's first meal there, he hit the dog. The whole place was wonderful but completely mad. You'd order a fruit salad and half an

Anxiety

Anxiety is our normal response to stress or danger. A little doesn't do you any physical or mental harm, but it can become a problem if the anxiety gets out of proportion to the situation causing it.

When you are anxious, a hormone called adrenalin is released into your blood and affects how you think, feel and behave. Some of the problems associated with anxiety include:

• negative thoughts, fearing you might faint, over-concern about your health, being afraid of everything
• feelings of tension, an increased heart rate (above 100 beats per minute at rest), sweating, shortness of breath, feeling trembly
• frantic behaviour, rushing around uselessly, eating more, smoking more, biting your nails, not being able to sit still for a minute

A vicious cycle can begin: anxious thoughts produce anxious feelings which you then feel anxious about, and so it goes on, round and round.

What can you do to control anxiety?

Learn to relax. This is a skill, and doesn't simply mean collapsing in an armchair. You can still feel anxious doing that. It means consciously learning to relax different parts of your body. Here are some tips:

• sit or lie so that you are comfortable, close your eyes and let your body grow heavier and more relaxed
• breathe slowly in through your nose and out through your mouth
• if distracting thoughts come into your mind, think about something that you find relaxing, like the warmth of the sun on a beach
• tense up various parts of your body in turn to the maximum, and then consciously relax them as much as you can

Try doing this for ten minutes a day, and whenever you feel panicky feelings coming on.

Stress

Everyone suffers from stress, anxiety and tension at some time. Travelling, taking exams, going for job interviews, are all particularly stressful, as are many other new situations.

There's evidence that a reasonable amount of exercise makes you better able to deal with the stresses and strains of life. It's more effective than drinking or smoking in helping you to relax. In a recent experiment, one group of volunteers did twenty minutes vigorous exercise three times a week, and a second group did very little exercise. Researchers then measured anxiety and tension levels. Those taking exercise came out best. The message is:

• walk or cycle rather than using the bus or car
• find a sport or exercise you enjoy and do it
• exercise for fifteen minutes three days a week
• use stairs rather than lifts

You can manage all this while travelling or when at home. It won't guarantee a stress-free life (life would be boring if it was), but at least you should be able to cope with it better.

hour later they'd produce a chicken curry, but that evening it really didn't matter, as Sally and he danced the night away to Led Zeppelin and Barry White.

As the night wore on, Jim began to wonder if Sally was expecting him to make a pass at her. He didn't want to, he needed a rest from the complications of relationships, but as their conversation grew more intimate, Sally, as if sensing his dilemma, dropped a bombshell. 'What,' she asked the startled Jim as they circled lazily around, intoxicated by the music, 'is wrong with a sexual and emotional relationship between women, if love, respect, reciprocity of feeling and egalitarian sexuality are at the core of it?'

Jim wasn't up to answering that one, and wasn't even sure he understood what 'egalitarian' meant. 'I went to a Catholic girls' school,' she continued, taking advantage of Jim's silence, 'where I learnt that sex was something that only happens between a man and a woman, within marriage, and that masturbation was wrong and homosexuality "unnatural". The word "lesbian" was used by girls there, not as a simple descriptive term but as a term of accusation and abuse. But I knew I was different.' Jim was beginning to feel that this was heavy stuff, but there was no going back.

'I knew that my attraction was to other women, and that this feeling was far too strong to be dismissed as simply a teenage "crush". I did try and trample down my feelings of sensuality, and the most difficult part was hearing myself saying "I'm gay" to another person for the first time. It was to my family doctor. I'd never discussed an emotional problem with her before. I thought it might be regarded as a trivial matter to talk to her about, compared with the problems of her other patients. I can't tell you how relieved I was to tell someone about it, which is probably why I'm telling you now.'

Jim begged for them to sit down. He'd suddenly began to feel exhausted. It wasn't that he didn't want to hear any more, just not to have to listen standing up. 'I'd kept so much fear, so much confusion and worry inside me for so long. Now I see my sexuality not as a "preference" or "a choice" – it's just something I am. I wasn't sure about telling my straight friends. At first I thought they might reject me – but they didn't, and in fact I think it's brought us closer. Even telling you now, not knowing you, I find a lonely, painful experience; but I think it helps me, and my acceptance of myself as a lesbian.'

Jim knew he was being offered something precious, a glimpse into someone else's most intimate and painful feelings, but he also felt out of his depth. He was aware that some of his friends were gay. Occasionally someone had even made a pass at him – like the American on Bali. Sally wasn't asking for sympathy, it was just something she wanted to tell him. A few moments later, she kissed him on the cheek and disappeared off into the night.

Next day Panchai persuaded Jim to hire a motorbike, and with Sally riding on the back of Panchai's they set out to explore the other side of the island. They stopped along the way at a temple offering a ten-day course in self-indulgent soul-searching for over-tense Westerners. Jim read the rules. 'No smoking; up at 5 a.m. every morning, or earlier if you choose; no eye contact or communication with other participants; two meals a day; do not ask the monks too many questions, as this will make them feeble, weak and sick and the consequences may lie on your conscience.' Not, he decided, the place for him. It also occurred to him that there is so much that stinks about being a traveller. It's like being a voyeur into other people's lives – then saving everything up for stories and a good laugh when you get home.

What lay ahead of them on the bikes turned out to be one of the most physically demanding, mentally stressful, and dangerous trips of Jim's life. It ended leaving him shaking with physical exhaustion, saturated with sweat, covered in dust from the spinning wheels, and bleeding

Chances of meeting a violent end in various countries

Country	Rate of violent deaths
US	8.7 per 100,000
Hungary	4.2
Australia	4.1
Belgium	3.2
UK	1.7
Greece	1.5
Japan	1.4
Norway	1.0

So you are ten times more likely to meet a violent end in America than in Norway, but it's still VERY UNLIKELY to happen anywhere.

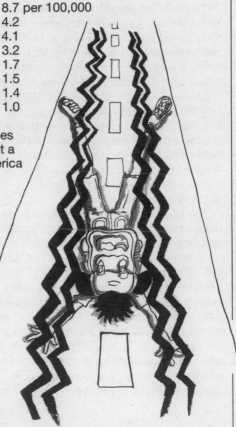

badly from a wound where he'd gashed his knee on a passing rock. Emerging from the other side of the mountain would have been exhilarating if he hadn't been so wiped out, and it took a day of swimming and lying in his hammock for him to recover.

His knee needed attention, so he tried the local doctor's surgery, held in a shack across the road. The light was so poor that the doctor worked with a torch. Without consulting Jim, he poured hydrogen peroxide into the wound and then proceeded to use a razor to scrape away the pus, loose gravel and flesh. By the time the doctor had finished, Jim felt five times worse than when he'd walked in, and looked like a war casualty. The doctor had the initials 'US' after his MD qualifications on the wall, which Jim was later informed meant he'd been found '*un*satisfactory' in his medical examination.

That evening, after a curiously sad farewell to Sally, Jim took the night ferry back to the mainland, and an overnight train to Bangkok. In the latter he had a westernized air-conditioned sleeper, clean and well organized, with two bunks one above the other and a corridor down the middle. He arrived in Bangkok at dawn, and taking a taxi to Kay San Road found the GB guesthouse and slept for a couple of hours.

His first priority was to pick up his visa for India. He then spent the rest of the day exploring Bangkok, just jumping on buses and getting off if he saw something interesting. In the Temple of the Reclining Buddha, he saw a giant Buddha called Wat Pho, over forty metres long, covered in gold leaf and with intricately carved mother of pearl feet. As he was walking past, a smooth Thai asked him if he wanted to buy some opals. Jim had heard of this scam from other backpackers, but it was his last day in Thailand and he felt he had nothing to lose. He was taken to a carpeted, air-conditioned room where there were two Thai girls. One did try selling him opals, while the other one tried selling him herself. She

Cuts

Most cuts can be dealt with by using a plaster. However, sometimes the cut will be too deep, the flesh at the edges of it won't come together, and the bleeding won't stop. If this is the case, the first thing to do is stop the bleeding, which is best done by putting direct pressure on the wound. This flattens the blood vessels in the area and slows down the flow of blood so that a clot can form. Because the force of gravity speeds up blood flow, it helps decrease the blood flow if the cut is raised higher than the heart. So if you cut your foot, lie down and raise your leg. (Obviously there are bits you can't do this with, without standing on your head!)

There are specialized strips of plaster called steristrips (useful to carry with you) which bring the wound together and quite often save you needing a stitch. But if the cut still gapes, or continues bleeding, see a doctor or a nurse and get it stitched.

Make sure you're up to date with tetanus injections. If you haven't had a booster within the last ten years and you're about to travel abroad – get one.

Sexual intercourse

If you thought there were a lot of words for getting drunk, try a few for sexual intercourse. Here are some from America: making love, having sex, fucking, bonking, doinking, getting it on, getting horizontal, ripping, the long hard bone job, screwing, humping, squashing, jumping, forming a sexual sandwich, pumping, letting her have it, filling the doughnut, putting the stem in the apple, bed-busting, riding the hobby horse, bumping, thumping, disturbing the neighbours, going all the way, headboard bouncing, fronding, quiffing, spontaneous combustion, piston popping, ball busting, creaming, lubing, heating it up.

was staggeringly beautiful, and said, 'Do you want to take me to a dance tonight? Won't cost you any money.' Jim refused.

On that last night, he hadn't planned to go to the red light district of Bangkok, but he nevertheless allowed himself to be persuaded by three German backpackers he'd met on the train the previous night. They walked along past stalls selling so-called Rolex watches, T-shirts, and toys, and past a selection of bars, night clubs, and sex shows – all selling girls in see-through dresses, and numbered so that you didn't even have to pronounce their names. He'd been warned all the way to Bangkok that you had to be self-disciplined there to resist the temptations of the flesh. The girls cost hardly anything and when the group Jim was with finally settled in one of the bars, six of them almost instantly attached themselves to him like octopuses, their hands going everywhere, touching him up with their eyes, which said, 'I'm all yours, sunshine.' One of them, much younger than the others – fourteen or fifteen at the most – kept staring at him with pale green eyes. She was the most beautiful person Jim had ever seen, and here she was for the taking. But the taking was for money, and again Jim managed to resist.

Going on behind all this was a live sex show on stage. No condom was used and it was all done with stale, bored expressions. It seemed that in Amsterdam, Bangkok or anywhere else, live sex shows were low on eroticism. Why the hell did anyone go to them, he wondered, if not by accident like himself? When the girl left the stage, she began plying for trade among the clientele in the bar. It was all too much, even for experienced and hardened travellers like themselves. They finished their beers and asked for the bill.

When it came, it was greeted with stunned silence. Then one of the Germans turned to Jim, pale-faced, saying, 'They want 2,600 baht. That's over $100 for our

More on drugs

Cannabis (grass, pot, ganja)

Cannabis comes from a plant called *Cannabis sativa*. It grows wild in many parts of the world. The vital ingredients are the tetrahydrocannabinols (THC). These are mostly found in the resin at the top of the plant. Hash or hashish is the commonest type of cannabis used in the UK. The resin is scraped or rubbed off the plant and made into browny-black blocks. Grass, dope, ganja or marijuana is a less strong greenish preparation made from the dried and chopped leafy parts of the plant. The strength of all these different types of cannabis can vary. The resin is usually mixed with tobacco and smoked. Grass can be smoked on its own. It can also be made into a drink or put in food.

The Chinese have used cannabis as a herbal medicine since the first century AD, and it has also been used for fun there, and in India. It was used in Queen Victoria's time to cure all sorts of ailments, and it was first made illegal in the UK in 1928. In the 1960s it became fashionable to use it, and 80% of all drug offences are to do with cannabis. The laws on cannabis vary in different countries. In the UK, it is illegal to grow, produce, possess or supply it.

Is it safe, is it nice?

Being in trouble with the police certainly isn't good for you. When smoked, cannabis can make you feel relaxed, talkative, sociable – though sometimes it has the opposite effect of making you feel panicky, anxious and suspicious. While under the influence of cannabis, your short-term memory may be affected, and your ability to drive, or perform other intellectual or manual tasks. The effects start a few minutes after smoking, and last one to three hours, depending on the amount taken.

Probably the occasional smoke of cannabis is pretty harmless, but there is evidence that frequent use is not good for you. As it is smoked with tobacco, it can damage your lungs. It can also cause brain damage, and heavy users may appear withdrawn and apathetic, will lack energy and do badly at work or school. Beware – cannabis has special risks for people with existing or underlying mental illness. It can cause delusions and psychotic breakdowns.

Does cannabis lead on to hard drugs?

Most people who use heroin will have previously used cannabis, though only a small proportion of those who try cannabis do go on to use heroin. Some argue that if cannabis were legal, fewer people would go on to hard drugs, because those who smoke it wouldn't come into contact with hard drug pushers. But the reverse could be true, and it could result in more people wanting to experiment with hard drugs.

Is it addictive?

What do we mean by addictive? Like it and want it? Can't do without it? There's no doubt that many people who use cannabis from time to time, or even every week, don't need to have it but enjoy it when they use it. However, those who use it intensively (three to ten, or more, times per week) get problems. They get apathetic and aimless, and may suffer brain damage. People who use

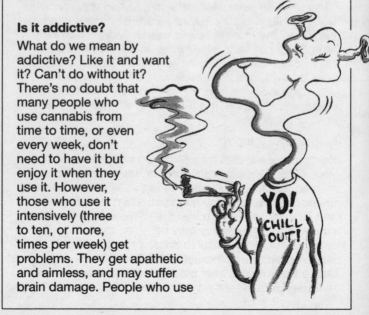

it a great deal get withdrawal symptoms, so 'yes' it is addictive.

What is the law?

Different countries have different laws. Some countries are more lenient than others about imposing the law on individuals who are using cannabis for personal use. If you are going to smoke pot around the world, find out what the local attitude is first.

For instance, marijuana is sold legally in restricted outlets like coffee shops in the Netherlands. Spain and Italy are reviewing their laws. Austria, the Cameroons, and West Berlin have strict laws but don't always impose them for personal use. In America, it's not actually legal anywhere, but different States vary over how they impose the law.

AIDS in Thailand

Of Thais tested for AIDS:

- in 1987, 100 tested HIV positive
- in 1988, 2,901 tested HIV positive
- in 1989, 13,600 tested HIV positive

Unofficial figures suggest that in 1991, 30,000 will be HIV positive, and that by 1994 the figure will be 1,000,000. 40% of heroin users in Bangkok are now infected with the AIDS virus.

In a recent study in one city in Thailand – Chiang Mai – over 72% of 'low class' prostitutes (those charging less than 50 baht) were HIV positive. The equivalent figure for 'higher class' prostitutes (those charging 50 to 100 baht) was 30%, and for prostitutes charging more than 100 baht the figure was 16%. A case of getting 'more', the less you pay!

six beers. No way can we pay it.' Immediately an argument developed with the Germans shouting at the manager, and the manager saying, 'Be cool – no trouble – that is the bill for the show, for the girls, for the beer.' One of the Germans turned to Jim. 'You'll have to get the police. We're not paying this.' Jim walked quickly towards the door, where a topless girl, in response to a sign from the manager, gave him a ravishing smile, put her hand up, and clicked the lock shut.

Jim knew he had to stay calm. He had all his money on him in his money belt – he was leaving the next day – and he didn't need this. It was too late now, but he knew what they should have done. They should have sorted out the price ahead of time, as soon as they'd come in. This was a cardinal mistake. He backed away as the girl clicked the lock open again and six muscular heavies came after him. The hundred-dollar bill began to look small as payment to get out of there. Maybe he should offer to pay, with the money Cindy had returned.

Jim was preparing himself to fight, knowing they would all get badly smashed up, when one of the German guys started explaining to the manager that he'd met one of the local police chiefs at a bar earlier in the evening. Miraculously, he even remembered his name. This incident was embroidered into something much more definite than it had been. It was mentioned in every other sentence, while pointing out also that $100 was impossible – they just didn't have it. The manager weakened, shrugged his shoulders, and signalled to the heavies who, though they didn't actually physically throw them into the street, leant on them jostling the whole way, and then spat at them as they walked off. Jim felt contaminated by the city. Bangkok had lost all its charm and he was thankful he was on his way out.

17 INTO INDIA, OUT OF AFRICA

Five-thirty in the morning is few people's best time of day, and even after considerable practice, it still wasn't Jim's. He'd sat on the plane from Bangkok drinking a variety of obnoxious brews out of tiny glass bottles. Wandering off the plane in a disorientated haze, his first impression of India was of yet another huge international airport, a cavernous bazaar full of standing figures wrapped in blankets, and supervised by what appeared to be a battalion of soldiers with sten guns.

Waking a sleeping backpacker departing for Bangkok, he swapped his *South-East Asia on a Shoestring* for *India – a Travel Survival Kit*. (No money changed hands – just a straight unambiguous exchange to the benefit of both. Why couldn't more of the world act the same way, Jim wondered?) Next he needed to discover how much the journey to the centre of New Delhi should cost. The airport information desk was closed, but a soldier standing guard nearby ventured, 'About 10 rupees.'

Outside the terminal stood a slouched row of black limousines, silent and slick as oil with darkened tinted

Your ears in aeroplanes

What makes your ears feel so peculiar when you go up and come down in an aeroplane?

The atmospheric pressure is greater on the ground than at altitude. Planes cruise at about 30,000 feet. The pressure of the passenger cabin is kept equivalent to the atmospheric pressure at 5,000 to 7,000 feet. A passenger plane climbs to this height in approximately thirty minutes. For the first 200 to 300 feet there is not enough pressure change between the different parts of your ears to cause problems. Above this height, different pressures in various parts of the ear cause your ear-drum to bulge, stretch and give you pain. The bulging occurs when the inner bit of the ear is at the greater pressure (left over from ground level) and the outer ear is at the same pressure as the aircraft's cabin and continuing to decrease until the plane reaches 5,000 to 7,000 feet. When coming down, the pressures on the ear are reversed.

However, the middle part of the ear has a small tube between it and your mouth called the Eustachian tube, which is closed except when you swallow. When the Eustachian tube opens, the pressure between your mouth and the inner ear equalizes. Therefore when taking off and landing you want to open the Eustachian tube as often as possible. Normally swallowing occurs every three minutes when you're asleep, and every minute when you're awake. If you chew you swallow more often, which is the theory behind chewing gum or sucking a sweet when going up or coming down in a plane. The best way to equalize the pressures, is to pinch your nose, close your mouth and swallow. If that doesn't work, try gently blowing against your pinched nose.

If you have a cold or ear problems when you're about to fly, use a decongestant. This stops the lining of the Eustachian tube getting swollen, when it would block off the entrance to the middle ear and stop the pressures equalizing.

windows. Luxurious safe-deposit boxes, Jim reflected, for ambassadors to be locked away in, all crisp and clean, and then transported in air-conditioned sterility, to be regurgitated into the safety of their embassies. A very different world from his, he pondered, as his rucksack was seized from his hands and flung into a baggage compartment by an employee of one of the bus companies, while he was herded aboard with much gesticulation and shouting. The ticket, which should have cost 10 rupees, actually cost 30 rupees and though a quick calculation would have told him this still only represented 50p, what mattered to him was that he was getting stung again. He was too well seasoned a traveller to like being taken for a ride.

On the half-hour trip into New Delhi, under wheeling vultures in the grey early morning light, Jim was aware through the slits of his weary eyes of straggling pyjama-clad figures, single and in groups, walking along the road in the same direction as the bus. They passed the fortified house of the Prime Minister and drove on through endless road blocks. Unable to sleep, he idly perused a local paper discarded on the seat next to him, and his eye fixed on an item in English:

'Two women admitted to the Jayaprakash Narayan Hospital have alleged that they were set ablaze by their husbands. 18-year-old Prabha, who was brought there from Zafrabad village, said in a statement that she had been harassed by her husband and her in-laws ever since her marriage, six months ago. Her husband would not even allow her to visit her parents occasionally, she stated. It seems her husband poured kerosene over her clothes and set her ablaze.

The other woman, 25-year-old Sajda, had initially said when admitted to hospital that she had suffered her burns through a kitchen mishap in her home. Later the victim admitted that her husband had set her alight. He had been harassing her for her failure to bear a child and because he thought she was not good-looking.'

Indian domestic life looked complicated, Jim thought.

Getting off the bus, he was hit by a wall of sensations. Dirt, dust, traffic din, cloying heat and a commotion of smells summoning up many unwanted associations. Sweat, spices, faeces, urine, wood-smoke and diesel oil were among the mixture of fragrances which wafted off the street. He'd been warned about Delhi – but he still wasn't prepared for it. The people and the poverty were overwhelming in his dazed and exhausted state. He was beginning to wonder whether he could take any more. There was nowhere to shelter from the storm of sensations, no base, no haven to rest in and take stock. Could this be the beginning of travellers' 'burn-out'?

To ward off the encroaching panic, he took the first tiny room he found, for 150 rupees, in Sunny's guesthouse near the Janpath market, only a short distance from where the bus had dropped him off. It was full of travellers, most of whom slept huddled next to one another in a cramped dormitory under corrugated iron on the roof. It seemed to Jim a claustrophobic nightmare, but they paid only 30 rupees a night. Outside, against the wall of the guesthouse, lay rows of bundled figures, their white clothes pulled over their heads and covering everything but the cracked, shiny skin of a line of small brown feet.

Jim lay naked on his bed throughout the endless morning, dimly aware in his sweating restlessness of the street noises and the movement of a slit of sunlight from the shutters climbing across his wall. Finally he had to face Delhi again, the sun sending him staggering out into the density of the streets. The air was full of dusty light and the ever-powerful smells, and the traffic was fierce with screaming scooters, revving engines, car horns, until he passed through the cool, vaulted arcade of the Lahore

Gate into the sudden peace of the gardens and pavilions of the Red Fort.

There he sat on a wall overlooking the banks of the Yamuna river, where rope climbers, tame monkeys, and snake charmers operated far below, and browsed through his recently acquired edition of the travel survival guide. He began with an invaluable section on 'Facts About the Country'. The history bit was fine, but what he enjoyed most were little snippets like:

– on railway waiting rooms 'These are free places to rest your weary head. The trick is to rest it in the comfortable 1st class waiting room, not the crowded 2nd class one.'

– on women travellers 'India doesn't present the problems for solo women travellers that some Asian countries can . . . The light cotton draw-string skirts that so many Western women pick up in India are really sari petticoats, and to wear them in the street is rather like going out half dressed.'

– on theft 'Never leave those most important valuables in your room; they should be with you at all times.' (Elsewhere it also suggested that a padlock is an essential item for locking rucksacks to luggage racks, and so on.)

– on tipping 'The term "baksheesh", which encompasses tipping and a lot more besides, aptly describes the concept in India. You "tip" not so much for good service but to get things done. A "tip" to a station porter will ensure you a seat when the train is packed out to the very limit.'

The section on the caste system explained that at the top are the Brahmins, who are the priests and the arbiters of what is right and wrong in matters of religion and caste. Then come the Kshatriyas, who are soldiers and administrators, then the Vaisyas, the artisan and commercial class, and the Sudras, the farmers and peasants. At the

Bites

Some people's skin reacts more to certain insect bites or stings than other people's. But being sensitive to one kind of bite doesn't mean that you will be sensitive to them all.

Some people get bitten more than others, which is probably related to the odours they give off. Because of

this, some of the insect repellents are simply smells that insects don't like.

If you do get bitten by an insect, and it swells up or is very itchy, taking an antihistamine by mouth will help. Putting calamine lotion or a hydrocortisone cream on the bite also helps.

Bed bugs

There are over thirty species of bed bug and they are all keen on sucking human blood. They hide away during the day and crawl out at night to get at your arms, legs, face – anywhere that is exposed. They then spend several hours digesting your blood. Although their bites irritate, unlike many insects, bed bugs don't seem to spread any nasty diseases.

Bed bugs are controlled by standard insecticide sprays, but if you move your bed away from the wall and keep a light on, you improve your chances of not being bitten.

Lice

Most people have had head lice as children. There are also clothing lice and crab lice which can both be a nuisance. Lice are spread by direct contact between people or their clothes. You know you've got them because you get itchy bites. Crab lice love pubic hair and can be transmitted during sexual intercourse. Condoms don't help here. Treatment is a special shampoo. Clothing lice are destroyed by washing your clothes in very hot water.

Fleas

Flea bites tend to occur in groups around the ankles and waist. The fleas are difficult to catch because they're small and they jump. Some people become expert at squashing them between their thumbnail and finger – but it takes practice and a very hard squeeze. If you find one, you're probably infested with them. Insecticide sprays help get rid of them – clothes and body.

bottom are the Untouchables, now renamed Harijans or 'children of God', who have no caste and who perform the most menial and demeaning of jobs (like cleaning lavatories). In the old days, if a Brahmin using the same temple as an Untouchable was touched by one, or even came into the shadow of one, then he was polluted and had to undergo a series of cleansing rituals.

The last invaluable bit of information Jim gleaned during his reading was that 'There is a post office at 9A Connaught Place, but New Delhi's efficient poste restante is on Market Street (officially renamed Bhai Vir Sing Marg).' Outside Lahore Gate, a beggar woman, her face completely disfigured from a burn, clutching an emaciated baby covered with fly-feeding sores, grabbed at his arm. Horrified, Jim gave her all the coins he could find in his pocket without working out what they were worth. She relinquished her grip as he hailed an auto rickshaw, a decrepit contraption with three wheels and a violent two-stroke motorcycle engine. The exhaust was pouring forth solid lead lumps and a virtual smoke screen. Jim negotiated the fare to Market Street with the Sikh driver before mounting, noting his comment that 'Things are very bad here for the Sikh. Life's not worth living.'

Two letters sat waiting for him – one as fat as a pregnant carrier pigeon, the other as thin as an anorexic one. The fat one (just what he needed) was from Penny – and postmarked London.

◻ ◻ ◻

1st March

Dearest Jim – Hope you got my last letter with the good news! Sending a letter off is a bit like sending out the dove from the Ark – hoping it won't come back. Noah must have felt much the same way. I haven't heard from you yet – but that's no great surprise. I'd looked forward to finding something waiting when I got back, but no luck. Maybe it's because you're so busy doing macho things, you can't be bothered to communicate; or maybe it's because you weren't expecting me to be back by now. Things turned out a bit differently from what I'd planned.

I moved on from Tanzania as I'd paid in advance to join a truck in Nairobi – organized by Hobo trans-Africa and setting me back a further £200 for six weeks, not bad really. There are a lot of these package tour organizations around – you meet them over and over again because they all do practically the same routes. Our truck was an old egg delivery vehicle with all the insides taken out and seats put in instead, and a cage to put the backpacks in. It was big enough to take twenty-four and two drivers, but when I was on it we were only twelve, none of them Africans.

We went back through Tanzania (that's where I wrote to you from last time), though a different part, and then on to Malawi and Zambia – nearly 1,000 miles altogether – and very fast because of the cholera epidemic. This was mainly in Lusaka, but it was all over Zambia too. We couldn't drink the water, shower, or eat tomatoes, cucumbers or melons. So mostly we ate cabbage, carrots, potatoes and onions, and some meat and fish. In Uganda we'd gone mad on fish because of the fish market they had in Kampala. The meat most of the time just wasn't worth the effort of cooking it. And people imagine you're going to have all these tropical fruits – but we couldn't get them. Even fresh vegetables we could only get every two or three days, so we had a lot of tinned stuff with us. I missed tomatoes most, particularly as tomato purée was ridiculously expensive.

You had to think carefully about everything – even how you washed your hands. We had our own water which we'd got in Malawi, and even this was bright yellow. When we were cooking, bits of this and that floated to the top – it was really disgusting. Going to the toilet could be a problem too. When the trucks stopped in the desert, you can't imagine how difficult it was to get any privacy. We'd walk miles away and still be in sight of everybody across the flat sand. The light has this funny trick of making people seem still right next to you. In the towns along the way the lavs were disgusting – always blocked up, stinking, and with flies buzzing around, or they were those kind of trays on the ground. In the villages they were usually just a bucket in the ground, so it seemed a great deal more hygienic to wait till you were under way again and go at the roadside, with or without an audience. We did have a spade for covering up our shit to try and be hygienic for other people. After all, you never knew who'd been there before you or might be there after you. In a bar or café, it was simply 'Go outside and help yourself.' And while we are on the subject of these little delicacies of life, before we left the women were told to take enough Tampax for at least a month longer than they intended to be away, because nothing like that is available over there. I was thinking that personally I wasn't going to need any for the next nine months. (I can laugh about it now, but I certainly couldn't then. And anyway, if I had been pregnant, I wouldn't have gone.)

As far as health precautions were concerned, what was particularly ridiculous was that when we arrived at the border of Zambia there were just these two blokes in uniform who gave us little bits of card saying, 'You are now entering a cholera area. Do not drink the water.' That was all, except that in minute letters on the other side it said, 'If you feel ill in the next 24 hours, go directly to a clinic,' but it didn't give you any other advice, and anyhow what clinic? There didn't appear to be any. Apart from this, we were given two tablets each. They didn't say what they were, or how we should take them, so we just presumed they were some sort of antibiotic. During the next part of the trip, one of our group thought she had cholera, so we pooled all our tablets together. She was being sick and had very bad diarrhoea. I didn't think she had it, but the driver rather fancied her and was particularly worried. We all got diarrhoea on and off — I got it from the yellow water in Malawi. There was a first-aid kit on the truck — just general things like plasters and antiseptic, and Imodium tablets for diarrhoea. That's what I took.

We used to chat about not sleeping with people when we were travelling (as if I would, after my recent experience with you!), and about not getting AIDS. Mainly joking, but I think it was on everyone's mind. When I was in Nairobi, I was told that 25 per cent of young men and women there are HIV positive. When I was sitting in a bar waiting to meet the people I was going on the truck with, it struck me that one in four of the people around me might have AIDS. There were a lot of prostitutes around if someone wanted to find one, but who'd take that kind of a risk? In fact, a couple of blokes did go off and sleep with prostitutes and all the talk was about how stupid they'd been and how they must have wanted to commit suicide. A few people in the truck paired up (not me you'll be glad to hear), but otherwise we were mostly celibate.

Another concern was that we should carry lots of 'oral rehydrate' stuff with us. It seems to be something everyone considers important over there. We'd all had cholera jabs before we left and got our certificates. And everybody had their own needles with them in case they had to have a booster. But I know now that a cholera jab only gives 50 per cent protection so it's the certificate that matters, so that you can get into the country, rather than the jab itself. Some of the people who had been with the lorry for more than six months were busy forging the date on their certificate so that they could get through Tanzania.

I took Autan out with me which I was told was the

best thing to repel insects – though people out there said it attracted the insects! We did sleep under mosquito nets. One night one of the drivers didn't bother to use one and next morning he had so many bites it was as if he'd come up in a rash. We all thought he was going to get malaria. I was wary about getting bitten because when I do, I tend to swell up a lot. I did get quite a few bites, but I don't know which ones gave me malaria. More of that later.

It wasn't hot all the time. People imagine it's boiling in Africa, but it isn't when it's the rainy season. We camped most of the time, but we always had to have two people in the truck on guard, especially near towns. We'd stop overnight and you'd think you were in the middle of nowhere, and then suddenly about twenty people would come out of the bush. I only managed a glimpse of each place we went through because we were travelling so quickly. I'm glad I had the time in Tanzania when we didn't move around so much and I could take everything in. The trouble about being on a set schedule was that you'd find this beautiful lake, or a market full of brightly coloured materials, and would want to stay and enjoy them and talk to the people, but we always had to move on. The children would cheer and wave as we went through villages, but I think the older people rather resented white people coming in truck loads to look at them. Can't blame them really, given the way that Western drug companies push artificial babies' milk at them – with instructions they can't read, and even if they could read, in the wrong language. Why can't they just leave them to breast feed naturally?

As you know, I left in December and planned to be back in May – probably after you. I'd arranged yet another truck run, this time with Trans Afrique. But then, as I've already mentioned (and hold your hat on, because I've survived!), I got malaria. We'd been given malaria tablets to take – yellow ones weekly containing chloroquine and white ones, two twice daily. I'd taken the weekly ones more or less religiously until Malawi, where the water was particularly bad. OK, so I missed the odd one but not often. Mind you, having diarrhoea on and off, I don't think they stayed in the system long, and I did forget my 'dailies' a few times. Not often – but when I took them out in the hospital, I had far too many left. It was bloody hard to remember. Out of fourteen people, only three were taking the daily ones. The rest thought that they didn't do you any good, and if you took the weekly ones, that was enough. And even then, most were taking the 'weekly' ones about every ten days, when they remembered.

Sunday was malaria tablet-taking day. People said the tablets made their hair fall out, their skin funny, and their nails brittle – in short, they claimed there were more bad effects from them than good. If I'd listened to them, I wouldn't have taken them at all. One statistic I've heard – I don't know how true it is – is that one in four overland travellers in Africa get some form of malaria, and probably because most of them don't take their pills.

Anyway, what happened to me is that we got off the truck at the border between Zambia and Zimbabwe to be stunned by the Victoria Falls. We found a bar there which stayed open till five in the morning, it was brilliant – just a local bar, we all went there. Next morning I was very headachy and sweaty and tired. I was dizzy when I stood up and began puking. I thought I had a hangover – I didn't realize. By the time I got to Harare, where I'd flown to see my relatives, I was feeling absolutely terrible. I had a temperature of 39.2°C, I couldn't get out of bed, and it just got progressively worse. It was then that I realized I was really ill and might have malaria. It's lucky I was in Harare, because it was quite easy to find a doctor. I had to pay, or at least my relatives did, but since then I've paid them back from the money I got from insurance.

Rabies

Rabies occurs in most parts of the world, but is very common in parts of South America, India, Thailand and the Philippines. Don't stroke stray cats and dogs in these countries, and beware of jolly chattering monkeys. There are 15,000 reported deaths from rabies each year world wide. If you are travelling to an area where rabies is common, and are going into the highways and byways – get immunized. The newer vaccines have few side-effects and are very effective.

If you do get bitten or even licked by a suspicious, angry animal, scrub the area with soap and running water for five minutes and then wash with alcohol (gin will do). Next, go and get a 'post-exposure' rabies vaccination. The time lag between the bite and the first signs of rabies is usually two to three months.

Malaria

What causes it?
Malaria is a disease caused by a parasite (an organism living in or on an animal) which is only visible under a microscope. The parasite is spread around by mosquitoes, and it's the female mosquitoes who cause all the trouble. They're the ones that make the whiny noise at night that keeps you awake – a noise like a sick aeroplane about to crash. But it's when the noise stops that you have to start worrying.

This is what happens. The female mosquito bites someone with malaria, sucks out their blood and with it the malarial parasites. These then develop inside the mosquito during the next seven to twenty days, and gather themselves together in the mosquito's salivary (spit) gland. When the mosquito bites some other poor unsuspecting sod, it injects some of its saliva, plus the parasites, into that person's bloodstream. The reason the mosquito injects the saliva is to stop the blood clotting while it is being sucked out.

The malarial parasites, once injected into the new victim, travel round the blood system to the liver. They wait around and mature further, and then invade the red blood cells where some of them go in for a bit of sex. Others remain celibate, but still reproduce. At this stage, the person with malaria is quite unaware of all this activity. Eventually the parasites burst out of the red blood cells into the blood, giving the person a high fever. Then another lot of cells get infected and the whole thing starts up again.

Do all mosquitoes carry malaria?

No. Some mosquitoes, like the ones in Italy and France, do not carry the malarial parasites. All you get if they bite is intense itching – annoying but not dangerous.

Where do you have to worry about getting malaria?

In total, about 105 countries in the world have malaria around all the time, but the main areas where you have to worry are Central and South America, Africa, India, and the Far East – including China.

How do you know if you've got malaria?

First, you have to have been in a place where you are likely to get it. If you have, and you've been infected, you get a fever, the sweats and shivering, a headache and tiredness. Stomach ache, jaundice and a coma can develop if it gets serious.

The interval between getting infected and having signs of malaria can be anything between five days and a year. If you have been in a malarial area and you get these symptoms any time during the next year, bear in mind that you might have malaria.

How common is malaria?

World wide there are, per year:

- 200 million malaria cases
- More than 1 million deaths

In the UK there are, per year:

- 2,000 malaria cases, all from people getting it abroad
- 10 deaths

How can you avoid getting malaria in a place where it is common?

- prevent the mosquito getting at you
- stop the mosquito biting you
- use medicines which prevent you from getting malaria

The best way of achieving these three things is to keep your flesh covered, sleep under a mosquito net, and take your anti-malarial medicines regularly.

What are anti-malarials?

These are drugs which kill the malarial parasites after they've got into your bloodstream. Unfortunately there is no one perfect anti-malarial, as some parasites have become resistant. So the type of anti-malarial you are advised to use may vary according to where you are going.

Chloroquine, Paludrine and Maloprim are the commonly recommended anti-malarials (there are many others), and they are normally taken daily or weekly. They should be started before you go away, and taken for six weeks after leaving the malarial area. A few people get side-effects from these medicines, but the side-effects are always much less bad than getting malaria!

Remember: Even if you are taking your anti-malarial tablets, if you get a 'flu-like illness it still might be malaria.

The doctor took a blood sample and some urine, and weighed me and poked me about a bit. The next day he came back and said, 'Yes, you're right. It's malaria.' I saw him every day after that, and he took two or three more urine and blood samples. The whole ten days was a haze I can hardly remember. I was very hot but felt cold and kept shivering. I felt so weak I couldn't even lift my arm up. I took one or two tiny sips of water at a time, even though I felt I wanted to take great gulps. If I took more, it all came back. I lost three kilos in three days.

The doctor gave me something called Fansidar and some antibiotics, but it wasn't until I got back to England that I had quinidine. He said I could fly home as soon as I felt well enough, so I was only out there for just under three months. I'd had all these great plans to travel round Zimbabwe, and I wanted to go to the Occa Fanga Swamps in Botswana (where I'd probably have got malaria, had I not got it already!) But I was feeling so ill, I just wanted to be at home in familiar surroundings.

It was horrible being ill away from home, though for the first few days I was so ill, I couldn't have cared less where I was. I was just sleeping the whole time, and trying to keep my pills down, which was a real problem. I didn't worry about getting AIDS or anything when the doctor started taking blood samples. I'd taken needles out with me, and a bottle of plasma, but when it came to the point, I felt too ill to remember to do anything about it. Afterwards, when the doctor heard I had the plasma, he accepted it as a present, because AIDS-free plasma is so valuable out there. Getting hepatitis was the other worry, though I'd had a jab of gamma globulin before I went, which is supposed to give fairly good protection. We were told not to have it out there, as the danger of what you might catch from the gamma globulin is even worse than hepatitis.

I didn't ring my mum until the worst was over. I knew

she'd insist on flying out, even though she couldn't afford it. And although I felt ill, I didn't think it was that serious. Getting ill won't stop me travelling in the future. After all, the risks aren't that high. I'm just as likely to get knocked down by a car at home. It might make me act a bit quicker in future. At first I didn't think it was anything serious, but the doctor said that if I'd waited any longer, I would have had cerebral malaria and black-water fever, and that would have been that. That did sort of shock me, as I never thought malaria could be that bad. Everyone else I'd heard of who'd had it had just been given a few tablets and got better in a couple of days.

When I got back, Mum and Dad met me at the airport and within two hours I was in hospital. I was taking quinidine for about ten days and that made me feel almost as bad as the malaria. I had buzzing in my ears and dizzy spells. I was nauseous and headachy. I stayed in bed for a while and didn't really feel well for about three weeks.

Frankly, I think if you want to stay healthy while travelling – DON'T listen to anyone who's been out there for three months and been lucky. Have all the injections. Take your tablets. Boil your water. It's not that much effort. Take a mosquito net and a good first-aid kit that's been designed for where you are going. I'm sorry if I'm a bit obsessed with all this disease stuff. You've probably been through similar experiences yourself by now.

I can't wait till you get back. I'm longing to hear about your adventures – or am I? I feel a bit apprehensive. We've been through such a lot. Will we be the same people?

All my love – Penny

□ □ □

God, what an earful! It made his expedition seem a bit tame, but as soon as he was back at Sunny's guesthouse Jim wasted no time in starting taking anti-malarial pills again. He was at least three weeks behind.

The anorexic letter, he realized much to his surprise, was from his sister. What the hell was she writing to him again for? His pulse began to rise slightly. No letter from his mum, and his sister writing for the second time – not regular at all.

□ □ □

Dear Jim – I don't know if I should tell you this, but I'm dead worried about Mum. I don't think Dad will have written, because he doesn't want to worry you – but *I have to tell someone*. She's in hospital because she's got breast cancer and has to have an operation. I don't think Dad wanted me to know, but I overheard him talking about it on the phone to Gran. It seems Mum's got to have the cancer cut out. I'm sure she's going to die, but I can't talk to Dad about it. He's all tied up coping with things, apart from anything else. Penny's back, and I did manage to have a good gab to her. She doesn't know much about it, but she doesn't seem to think it's all that worrying. Oh, God, I can't bear the thought of Mum dying. Tell me she won't!

Your very, very worried sis – Mary

PS   Please write *soon*.

□ □ □

Jim suddenly felt sick. He'd have to go home. He hadn't been sure before whether he could face India or not, and now he knew. He couldn't manage any more travelling, he'd had enough. All that making the same conversation over and over again, explaining who he was, where he was going, what he was doing. All those hassles over where the next meal was coming from and where he was going to spend the night. Cindy was in the past. America, Australia, Bali, Java, Sumatra, Thailand, Delhi – he'd done them all. He knew where he wanted to be, and that was home. If his mum was ill, he was needed and he was going. He wouldn't tell anyone – he'd just arrive.

18 WINGING HOME, DREAMING INDIA

The shit hit the fan at the local Air India Office. The woman Jim spoke to at the desk had sullen eyes. 'Do you speak English?' he asked. 'Sure, how can I help you?' Pathetically, Jim explained about his mother and his need of an urgent flight to London. She typed his name on to a waiting list on her computer and said she'd telex airport control. But Jim needed something more precise. 'When is the next definite free place?' he asked. She named a date four weeks away. 'Where am I on the waiting list?' 'I'm afraid there's no way of finding out.' He tried again. 'You must have the waiting list as you've just typed me in on it. Please tell me how many names there are.' He was trying to be calm. The woman phoned someone, typed in a bit more, and in a weary voice said, 'There are forty-five people in front of you on the standby list.'

He surely hadn't heard right. Fear and tears welled up. He was on his last legs. He wanted home. The tired, spoilt brat in him that had been lurking just below the surface for too long, suddenly took over. 'Look, I've been fucked around long enough. My mother's dying and I have to get on a plane – now!' A manager miraculously appeared from a back room. 'No problem, please. We'll sort something out. Please come into my office.' Ten minutes later, Jim was clutching a ticket for a flight to London the next day.

Having achieved what he wanted, for a moment he allowed guilt to take over. Perhaps there were other people in greater need, but the deed was done. His spoilt side had its uses, but he didn't like it any the more for that. A bribe might have been equally effective but seemed, to his warped westernized morality, even worse.

Next morning, in Delhi, he awoke at dawn with the cries of people mingling with the bird song. It flooded his mind in an instant that this was his last day here, the last day of his trip. Tomorrow he'd be home again with his mum and dad, his sister, and Penny. He heard the distinct cry of a single bird, and looking out into the courtyard saw a hoopoe with its orange crests erect. Above its head, dust clouds were painting pictures in the early morning sky. After tomorrow, there would be no more of this.

But it was in the aeroplane, winging home, that he got the full taste of India – by proxy. The neighbouring seat was overfilled by an oversized backpacker with overflowing verbal diarrhoea. Too much food and too many experiences too quickly, reckoned Jim, as he half-listened, offering an occasional nod. No encouragement was needed. She launched forth.

'You don't know what you've missed. Being in India made me feel I was part of something else, sort of merging in with everything around me, as if I was letting a massive wave of a new life sweep over me, but always with a feeling of anxiety eating into me – anxiety about dirt, poverty, my health, being ripped off, robbed, mugged.

'You were complaining about Delhi railway station, but I remember it as having the best tourist ticket office in any station anywhere. It's air-conditioned and we sat there for hours, all quiet and civilized and away from the chaos. I've been travelling with a friend, Fiona, and we were overwhelmed by Delhi. We wanted out fast as soon as we got there. We were heading south and the only certain train we could get to Madras was air-conditioned and first class, and cost about £27. We reserved places but still had to "tip" our porter to get our seats.

'We were in a carriage with two levels of bunk beds, the lower ones turning into seats. Next to us was this ancient crinkly Indian in a snowy white robe, like someone out of the Bible, mumbling away to himself. Maybe he was a latter-day Moses or someone, warning about plague, pestilence, madness and paranoia. Opposite us was a couple about our own age, with a baby boy called Akil. They spent hours showing him how to split peanuts and eat them, before putting him to sleep on the berth. His father stretched out beside him.

'We glided out of Delhi in the late afternoon with a wonderful feeling of total security and relief as we watched life through the tinted windows. We could see squatters in low sacking huts by the railway line, with bikes and rickshaws stacked all around. Men were squatting by open fires, or standing pissing, and I remember a group of Sikhs with turbans playing cricket on a mud space between the shacks. The women all wore saris and were blackened by the sun. They had bundles or pails on their heads. The woman sitting opposite told us, "Women are more united than men here. Men drink and make factions. Many Harijans now live in brick houses instead of mud huts because of women's work."

'Gradually, the houses and shanties gave way to fields growing maize, and in the distance, highlighted against the horizon, we saw a man stumbling behind a plough pulled by two oxen.' (It was just as Jim had found it

Diarrhoea and Vomiting (D and V)

It is difficult to travel and not have an attack of D and V at some point. It is part of the way of life. It's worth taking sensible precautions, but at the same time it would be crazy to wrap yourself in cotton wool and not experience local 'native' eating and drinking. Otherwise it raises the whole question of why you're travelling in the first place.

The cause of D and V is nearly always an infection by some bug or other that you have taken on board in what you've eaten or drunk, and that your body is not used to. For instance, in India you may eat food with a bacteria in it which is common there. Most Indians are resistant to it because they've grown up with the bacteria,

but you are virgin territory. The same Indians, if they came to England, might get diarrhoea from a bug that you are resistant to.

Some of the bugs causing diarrhoea are viruses, and the other organisms include E.coli, cholera, typhoid, giardiasis and amoebiasis. You can also get stomach upsets from gastritis due to over-indulgence in alcohol, but by far the most diarrhoea is caused either by a virus, or by different kinds of the bacteria E.coli that your body is not used to dealing with.

When is a shit a normal shit and when is it diarrhoea?

You know best – it depends on what you normally produce and we Brits don't usually discuss these things! Nor do we see much human shit, unless you are in the habit of examining your own, or some lazy sod forgets to pull the chain! (Many European toilet pans are specifically designed so that you can admire your production before flushing it away.) However, in spite of this, most of us know when we've got the squitters. It's mainly a question of degree.

Can you avoid getting diarrhoea?

No – not a chance in India, but you can cut down on the risks by ensuring all the cooked food you eat has been freshly and well cooked. You should also try and drink only bottled and canned drinks. In general, follow the warning, 'if in doubt boil it, peel it or forget it', but that may not always be possible, and you've got to eat and drink something and try and stay happy as well!

So you've got D and V – what should you do?

1. To begin with do nothing except drink lots of fluid and cut down on fatty and milky foods.
2. If it doesn't clear up in a couple of days, and you are otherwise well, don't worry – but you could try taking some Imodium tablets (see first-aid kit, Chapter 3). They won't kill off the infection, but they will slow down your gut, and make your life less uncomfortable and your bum less sore.
3. If you've got blood or mucusy white pus, don't fall off the loo – it doesn't mean you're dying. If you haven't got a fever as well, it probably means you've got amoebiasis (that single-cell lump of jelly you learnt about in biology). See a doctor and get some medicine for it (metronidazole is the usual one).
4. If you've got diarrhoea with blood, mucus and a fever, then definitely hit the local doctor for some medicine as you've got dysentery.

When to worry?

Most people get better quickly and easily. Those who don't, die from losing more fluid and salts than they take in. The treatment in India or elsewhere is exactly the same, so travel with sachets of a special salt solution called Rehydrat (see first-aid kit, Chapter 3). If you've forgotten these, or have run out, mix and drink (not all at once!) one litre of 'safe' water, one teaspoonful of salt and four teaspoonfuls of sugar. A can of flat Coca Cola is a good alternative.

elsewhere, scenes so primitive and yet viewed with the detachment of a westernized eye through the double glazing of an air-conditioned window.)

'The Indian couple on the train offered us all sorts of food – potato pastries, roti, sag, radish, sabji, pickle, purple onion, lassi, and peanuts in toffee cakes. Till then we'd been petrified about what we should eat. The first two days in Delhi, we'd survived off biscuits and mini Whispas we'd brought with us, washed down with bottled drinks. At the hotel, when we'd washed our hands, we'd put the plug in the basin and put steritabs into the water, but this was the first and last time, I'm afraid.

'That first train journey took us a day and two nights and covered over 2,000 kilometres. There was a system whereby we'd order a meal from a man in charge of our carriage, and he'd telegraph ahead to the next station and when we arrived there, the meal would be all ready in metal dishes and little packages. Whatever we ordered, however, it usually turned up as rice, dal and vegetable mash with yoghurt. The vegetable cutlets for breakfast when we got there were really tasty.

'We did get a bit hassled travelling around. We didn't dare accept an offer to go to someone's house for tea or anything, and when travelling third class we'd get touched up all the time. People would bump into us deliberately and try to feel our breasts. It was a real drag. It meant we couldn't get into discussions and had to dress reasonably well covered up. At one place, I think it was at Jag Falls, we thought we'd escaped from the hassle by climbing down these 1,400 steps, but there at the bottom was an Indian selling beer from a crate. He sat there watching us, pleading, "Please come behind these rocks with me. For two girls – how much?" All we could do was say, "Go away, go away." Finally we said, "Married," pointing to our fingers. He was terrified. "Oh, very sorry Mrs," he muttered and disappeared instantly. "Married" worked well, and burping in their faces was another deterrent. The problem is that because the porn videos there all show white women having sex, they assume we're all an easy lay. I was told that even the condoms in India have a picture of a white woman on them.' (Jim had a sudden guilty flash – Jane. Why hadn't he written back?)

'The second night on the train, I had terrible tummy pains and bad diarrhoea – Delhi belly – in spite of all our precautions. I had to crap through a hole in the grotty lavatory floor. Have you ever had to do that?' (There was no pause for a reply.) 'I swayed around with this terrible burning gut ache, squirting liquid for hours, my stomach churning again and again.' (Jim wondered if he could ring for the air hostess and ask to change seats.) 'I had a love/hate relationship with the food in India, always wanting it because it was so good and there were so many different things to eat, but hating it because it made me so ill. My guts haven't been right the whole time I've been in India, and was I glad of the bog rolls I stashed away in my rucksack! They were practically all I had with me, them and a supply of Tampax, but in fact I hardly had any periods while travelling.' (Christ, Jim thought, first squirting diarrhoea and now Tampax. If there was one thing he could do without right now, it was hearing about Tampax. Why did women have to be so communicative? Couldn't they bleed [or not] in silence?)

'We got into Madras, which is the capital of Tamil Nadu State, at about eleven in the morning on the second day. The landscape had got drier and drier all the way south. As we came into the station, we noticed bundles of beggars sleeping in rags on the ground, in the dust and dirt between the rails. There was much more hassle with cab drivers there than there had been in Delhi. We fought off most of them and Fiona and I piled our gear into a tiny cycle rickshaw. Our bus stand was a few kilometres beyond Madras. *India – a Travel Survival Kit* described it as "a well-organized, pleasant, easy-going city", but don't believe a word of it.' (By now, Jim had his own opinion of Lonely Planet travel guides, most of which were good, but he wasn't allowed a word in edgeways.)

'The buses were totally ramshackle and bog deep in puddles of pee. We'd been given the number of the one we wanted, but were told we should always ask, "Where does this bus go to?" rather than "Does this bus go to . . . ?" because in India people like to please and always answer, "Yes." We were heading for Kanchipuran, one of the seven sacred cities of India. We'd arranged to work at this Polio Centre for Children, but it didn't turn out to be much like what we'd expected. It is run by the Church of South India, and looks after about 140 children aged 3 to 16. If the local doctors are to be believed, one in ten children there gets polio. I don't know why they don't just immunize them all.

'We walked in and the people there looked at us and said, "Oh, yes – who are you?" When we explained we'd arranged to work there (back in England), they said, "Well, now you're here, you might as well stay." Not a great beginning, but we were given a big bare room with two beds in it, a large shuttered window, white walls, and an electric fan on the ceiling. The beds, the wooden sills of the doorways, the brass brackets for clothes, the handles of the water jugs, the bowls for food – everything at the centre was worn right down, even the water buffalo kept tethered near a disused swimming-pool in the compound and used for milk. The swimming-pool had been built for the children to exercise in but had never been used because of lack of water.

'We got our food but no pay – as officially we weren't there and they didn't really need us. As for the food, it was rice, rice and more rice, with very spicy vegetables. The children refused to eat anything unless it was very hot. But it was pretty poor stuff, and we didn't know how they survived. Occasionally, as a special treat, we'd be given jam and white sliced bread as the ultimate luxury. It was heaven.

'Sometimes we'd be woken at 4 a.m. by music from a local bazaar. One night we climbed out (they locked the gates of the centre at night), and wandered through the bazaar absorbing the food stalls, the workshops full of smoky tin boxes and worn implements, the advertisements and religious pictures. There were buffalo wandering round with us. Luckily we were with one of the Indian helpers, who had an infected toe and wanted to buy some antibiotics. The chemists were amazing. You could buy anything – valium or antibiotics, for instance – over the counter without a prescription, but what was on display was local and Western stuff mixed.

'Some days we'd watch the dhobi wallahs washing our clothes with huge blocks of soap, beating and pounding the garments with long bits of wood. We couldn't help wondering whether there would be anything left, and how they would know what belonged to us, as they seemed to be washing a million other items at the same time. Human labour's so cheap in India it made me realize how great it is having other people doing things like your washing . . .' (Jim had a sudden pang about his mother. Was she really dying? Please God, no! He couldn't imagine life without her. And not just because of his washing. The mouth next to him continued.)

'After a month, we left, and caught a train from Madras to Trichy, and then on to Quilon. We were heading for Kovalam Beach, near Trivandrum at the southernmost tip of India. It says in the guide – here, I'll read it out to you.' Compressing her rolls of fat, his travelling companion dived between her legs, dug out the all-too-familiar fat black paperback, shuffled through it and started to read:

'"It takes a little effort and time to get to Kovalam, and most people have given India a chance to seep into their veins by the time they arrive. This is one reason why you get such an interesting collection of people on the beach." Not bad, uh? When we got there, we found it wasn't like India, but was a westernized haven, a long way from the poverty and the other horrors of the Polio Centre. It was actually a series of small bays, separated by rocky promontories, all crammed with hotels and restaurants, and a few Indians who come to watch the tourists. We stayed in a beach cottage called the Aspara, with tiny rooms and two or three people in each.

'While we were recovering there, we had a mad four-day, "backwater" trip into the Kerala province, from Quilon to Alleppey. We'd get on and off these little open ferry boats, like local buses ploughing along canals, with palm trees and people living on each side, on narrow strips of land. During the day we sat on the corrugated roof, being cooked by the sun and watching life pass by on each side – families, animals, canoes with huge sails that I couldn't believe would stay upright. The ferry boat stopped all the time, but just for a few minutes – long enough to nip off for a cup of char and a pee. Then in the evening, we'd get off, find a hotel, eat a lot, and next morning we'd be back on a boat again.

'Next we took the train to Bombay. The harbour by the Gate of India is beautiful, in spite of the loads of skyscrapers around. There were beggars everywhere, and I was asked again and again if I wanted to sell dollars or buy hash. A friend of one of the blokes we met went bonkers from some drug or other he'd been taking. It was scary. He went completely mad, hearing voices all night long telling him to do things. No one was sure what he'd been on. In the end, he had to be shipped home. I personally wouldn't touch anything there. We wandered into the Taj Sheraton to use their loos and have a wash. It's full of super-rich people, but anyone, if they look right, can stray in. Bombay is full of shops and double-decker buses, and has shabby Victorian

Will population and birth control solve 'developing' world problems?

Parents only have smaller families when they are confident that their children will survive. In developing countries, children represent the same benefits as the Welfare State in Western countries. That is, the children help out when the parents are ill, or too old to work.

Increased wealth in a nation does not necessarily lead to an increase in family size. Instead, better education and better distribution of wealth leads to better family planning which decreases population expansion.

Plastic bags

All the wonderful uses for old plastic bags:

- smelly towels
- wet swimming costumes
- rubbish
- picnics
- dirty clothes
- first-aid stuff
- books, cameras, and so on (to stop sand and water)
- to keep your condoms in!

Invent a few more yourself:

....

....

....

....

....

....

....

....

Environmental problems of plastic

Plastic is a bi-product of the petroleum industry. In its present form, plastic is not biodegradable. This is because chemists have worked for years to make sure it isn't so that your plastic cereal bowl doesn't fall to pieces while you're eating. Now chemists are trying to make some plastic biodegradable again – so that it disappears in sunlight. No one has managed to make it truly biodegradable. At present the plastic just breaks down into pieces that are too small to be perceived by the human eye – but the stuff is still there.

Some plastics may take up to 400 years to disintegrate. It is about 400 years since Sir Walter Raleigh introduced tobacco into England, and we are still seeing the after-effects of that pollutant. When plastic is burnt, it produces dioxins. These are poisonous chemicals (50,000 times more so than cyanide) which are themselves not biodegradable and therefore last a very long time in the environment. The term 'dioxin' usually means the chemical is 2,3,7,8 TCDD. Dioxins are also found in leaded petrol, bleached white paper and weed killers. Cutting down on the production of dioxins means not using whiter than white paper products, using unleaded petrol in your car, and recycling your plastic bags.

In one week, between 20 May and 26 May 1990, five supermarket chains in Britain alone used 113,000,000 plastic bags!

houses with ugly rose windows. There were Arabs every-where. We didn't like Bombay, so we took a scruffy steam train, with flecks of soot pouring in through the windows, up to Ahmedabad. Along the way, people fed us abji, roti and jam. Everyone was so generous, always willing to share. Not at all like the blank stares you get on British Rail.

'Up and up we went, climbing into the . . . ' (Jim was beginning to fall asleep, missing great chunks of the dialogue.) ' . . . room overlooking a lake, around which there were lots of palaces . . . water level low because of drought . . . no rain for years . . . singing coming from temple . . . woken early by dhobis gossiping outside the window . . . town was stepped up around the lake, beautiful arched balconies, men and women with bare breasts . . . ' (Jim woke up again.) ' . . . washing them-selves in the water at the bottom of stone staircases, lathering themselves all over, the men swimming . . . other women on their balconies, dressed in pistachio green saris, with silver bangles on their ankles, combing their long black hair. We saw lots of birds on the lake, including divers, cormorants, kingfishers . . . ' (The voice next to him went on.) ' . . . the gardens, such beautiful views . . . untamed feeling about the people walking around, as if they'd come straight out of the desert . . . children played cricket below the temple on the lake shore, next to dozens of small lighted shrines winking their lights on the lake's still waters . . . I remember a puppet theatre in a courtyard, brilliant coloured puppets dancing, to a woman singing and playing the drum. One puppet was a man on a horse with two lighted torches doing acrobatics . . . beating a drum . . . others fighting, speaking with squeaky bird-like voices . . .' Jim fell fast asleep.

When he woke again, she was still at it, staring in front of her, as if in a trance. ' . . . the Maharajah's palace in Jaipur, which is made of pink stone. We had a ride on an elephant with floppy, dirty grey-black ears, mottled like banana skins, and a design chalked on its forehead, between tiny bloodshot eyes. When I got on, its hide felt rough and hairy. It was like riding a patient, swaying mountain, with an awful long way down each side. While I was on its back, a monkey stole my ice-cream. It had been watching me and suddenly swung down and snatched it out of my . . .' (Jim was off again . . . and back again.) ' . . . we thought Fiona had amoebic dysentery. She was bunging herself with Imodium. We bundled her on to a train, took twelve hours, hellish for her . . . on to Daramasalla, near where the Dali Lhama is exiled. We saw quite a cross-section of religions while we were in India. In the south, it was all very Christian and completely took over their lives. The Hindus were worried about their karma. If people were cheating us, we'd say, "But think of your karma." The Tibetans were so tranquil and relaxed after the south. We took Fiona to a Tibetan hospital and this lovely doctor gave her some pills. I don't know whether they did any good.

'I got my ears pierced in a local shop where they dipped the end of a needle in dettol and shoved it in. I must have been mad, not worrying more about what I might catch.

'The Taj Mahal was last. It was wondrous, like blooming sherbet, intensely and greatly beautiful. As we were leaving, I kept looking back, to make sure it was still there. Abstract spiritual perfection made solid, like a perfect delicious breas . . .'

Jim awoke with a start. An air hostess was shaking his shoulder. The seat next to him was deserted, except for a battered copy of *The Hitch Hiker's Guide to the Galaxy*. He picked it up. What page had he been at?

He put it down, the plane was empty, and outside his window rows of aircraft stood silent and forlorn on the shiny wet concrete of Heathrow airport. He stumbled off, swept along interminable corridors of glass, bemused by the chattering hordes of well-dressed people around him, the solid drizzle outside, the impassive people at passport control inside, on to the clatter of the baggage claim consoles bearing his battered rucksack towards him. He loaded it on to a crablike, wheel-jarring trolley, out through the green NOTHING TO DECLARE exit, trying not to make eye-contact with the white-shirted Customs officers. Out . . . out . . . out, shivering in the nervous, cold greyness of England. Why weren't his mum and dad there to meet him? Why hadn't he told them he was coming home? Who was it crying? He couldn't stop himself.

19 COMING HOME TO ROOST

Jim allowed awareness to creep slowly in. He hadn't opened his eyes yet. The tiny bit of his mind that was awake couldn't, didn't yet want to define where he was. Curled up in a sleeping bag on a mountainside in Java, lying on a carpet of flowers, a white-frothed rushing stream to one side and a smoking volcano above, silhouetted against a dark sky sprinkled with stars? Or in a losmen in Bali with the warmth of Cindy beside him and an erection stirring?

He inched his consciousness up a level. What was that scraping noise? No, he didn't need to look. It was the same old branch tapping on his window, the one his father had promised to cut off a year ago. He was safe in suburbia, in a house made of bricks, the nearest open countryside at least fifteen miles away across an urban jungle of tarmac, concrete, tiled roofs, street lights, and dog shit. Had anything changed, he wondered? Around him began the sounds of his family stirring – his sister running a bath, his mother in the kitchen making breakfast, his father pissing in the lavatory next door. Cradled but solitary in the warm cocoon of his sleeping bag (a habit he hadn't yet been able to give up), he let his mind slide back across the two weeks since his return.

The surprise had been complete. The house was deserted when he let himself in, glad to find that he still had his keys. There was only his cat, who treated him with the utter disdain of a stranger, showing neither fear nor love, standing silent and patient beside her feeding bowl. Jim had wandered disconsolately through the cold rooms, with an increasing sense of exhaustion and unreality, finally collapsing, still fully clothed, upon his bed and falling asleep.

He'd been wakened by the sound of his family. The front door had banged, followed by his mother's voice chiding Mary about not hanging up her coat, and Mary swearing at the cat for getting under her feet. Listening to them, Jim had been overcome by a terrible lethargy, suffocated by it and unable to move. He'd lain there for half an hour, until his mother had come into his room with a pile of clothes. She had screamed and then burst out crying at the sight of his precious, brown, unshaven form, then had descended on him and smothered him with hugs and kisses. The knowledge that he was still loved and wanted by someone clearly alive and well rent his heart. He was home at last.

Since then, it had been a whirlwind existence of pubs and old friends, including Penny and Frank. (Jane was still in Paris, but the others seemed to think she was OK.) His mum was over her operation, his sister still pubertal, his father still pontificating. Everything was continuing on course. The only thing that had totally changed was himself. Talking to Penny, the first time they were alone together, he'd been surprised (or had he?) to discover how little they now had in common. She had blank-walled him with a non-stop lecture about poverty in Africa (she was going back to work there), and had rushed off before he could unburden himself of any of his own adventures (or even what to her might seem his sins). His other friends hadn't been much better, expressing minimal interest while continuing a dialogue among themselves, over many pints of beer, about the latest football results, TV programmes and girlfriends.

In the end, none of it had worried him much. He had found within himself a confidence in his own abilities that had not been there when he left. He wanted to do something in the world – he was not sure what – maybe something ecologically green. Saving the Sumatra rain forests would do for a start. He had owned up to his parents about not sending off his UCCA/PCAS form, accepting their irritation as reasonable, and putting himself down in the 'clearing' system to go to a poly and take computer studies.

Furthermore, in spite of national rising unemployment thanks to the government's continuing stupidity, he had, through sheer determination, found himself a job in the local garage. The money wasn't great, but it was enough to cover his immediate financial needs, including paying his parents some money for his keep and repaying his dad's loan. And after an acute attack of bronchitis immediately after his return, he'd discovered he no longer wanted to smoke.

He felt as competent as the next person, reasonably in control, and able to fend for himself. He was an individual living organism, who had roamed the world and survived. OK, so it had taught him that he still had a lot to learn, but he looked forward to it with relish, mixed in with a healthy degree of anxiety about the unknown – accepting that this was the way life should be.

Slowly he climbed out of bed and wandered downstairs, following the rising smell of bacon, eggs and toast. Two weeks ago, he'd been woken in the morning, to the hot dusty streets of Delhi, by the cries of a hoopoe bird. Would he ever again, he wondered, wake to a field full of kangaroos, the smell of a wet rain forest, the sun rising over a white sandy beach?

He bent down and picked up a card from the doormat.

It was for him, it was from India, it was from Cindy, and it said: 'Nice one matey – I'm late but don't worry.' He started worrying.